Hell
to
Reality

One prisoner's journey

Best wishes

Jacob

ISBN-978-0-578-21872-4
10 9 8 7 6 5 4 3 2 1

Printed in the United State of America

Published by DNGU Publishing.

www.jacobbooks.com

Printed in the United States by Morris Publishing®
3212 East Highway 30
Kearney, NE 68847
1-800-650-7888

If you are going through hell, keep going.

--Winston Churchill

Table of Contents

Chapter I
War

I T WAS AUTUMN OF 1939. POLAND was besieged and surrounded. Germans had come in from the west and the Russians had invaded from the east. The population of Poland was in a bitter shock after such a rapid capitulation. The people then expected the worst. "Yes," Peter replied.

"You then speak, fluent German?" asked Shultz. They could not trust the Germans or, even less the Russians.

The fog hovered deep over the city. In the administration building of the Gestapo, Captain Shultz had received a list of people who were of German nationality, living in the city. "Execute the order immediately, tell them they will have no other choice, listen or be forced to cooperate with the Third Reich," said Major Muller.

"Yes, Major," said Shultz. Together with three soldiers; they obediently stepped into the car and drove away to execute the order.

The Mayer family lived in the town of Torun in the north of Poland. They had a nice home on a small, quiet, secluded street. It was early morning, and Peter and Mary were already on their feet. They were both preparing their vegetables in their garden to sell in the city market. A German staff car veered and stopped in front of the elegant two-story house; three soldiers quickly got out of the vehicle. "See who has come?" said Peter to Mary.

Mary peered out by the window and cried out, "Germans! What do they want from us?" Peter jumped to his feet.

"I do not know," answered Peter. They waited in fear anxiously; a heartbeat away from the full development of the situation.

German soldiers hurriedly entered the yard. Shultz impatiently knocked; abruptly, bouncing hard; he battered several times on the heavy wooden door and said, "You must open up Gestapo!" The door jerked open violently. Before them stood a frightened Peter. One of the soldiers arrested and pulled Peter out of the house and went inside; the other soldier pushed Mary out of the house. Peter and Mary were terrified.

"There are two children in the upstairs room. Should I pull them out as well?" asked the soldier looking at Shultz.

"That will not be necessary. Leave them alone. We will attend to them, later." Shultz replied.

The soldier turned to Peter and asked, "Are you Peter Mayer?"

"Yes. It is me," Peter replied.

"You were born in Munich?" asked Shultz.

"Yes," Peter replied; frightened, not knowing why he was asking.

"That means you're German. We need young, viral, strong men like you who know German. What other languages do you know?" Shultz retorted.

"Polish, Lithuanian and Russian," replied Peter.

"Those are the people we need for co-operation. You will sign a document that you will work only with us," said Shultz.

Peter said, "But, I have a Polish wife and two small children. How can I do that?" Impatiently, one of the soldiers hit Peter in the face. Blood began to pour from Peter's mouth.

"You are a German. It is your duty!" said Shultz to Peter. "If you do not sign the order now, I'll kill you, right in the street, like a dog!"

"I cannot," gasped Peter.

At this moment one of the soldiers put a gun to Peter's head and said to Shultz, "I must shoot him!" Mary began to cry, with deep despair. They were all unaware of two sleepy boys who stood near the door and began to cry aloud. Shultz looked at them. He had two boys himself; which he left at home, in Germany. He felt sympathetic for them.

"We will give them a little more time, until tomorrow. He may change his mind. We need young passionate people," said Shultz. The soldier hid his gun in his holster. "We're going," Shultz shouted to the soldiers. The squad went to the car that was parked in front of the house and drove off.

Mary and the children ran up to Peter and began to squeeze him tightly. Peter stood in shock, motionless. When he recovered, he embraced them all. "Let's now get inside," said

Peter and everyone walked into the house. Mary could not control her emotions after this incident.

Crying and hugging their small children, Vladek and John, she whispered, "What will happen with us now? Where will we go?"

"Let me think," said Peter. Mary and Peter went to the kitchen and sat down at the table discussing the whole situation. The event was very serious. Finally, Peter said, "I will not sign the list. I would have to report everyone, I know. I will not do that. I will have to run."

"But where?" asked Mary.

"For now, I'm hiding in the countryside. My mind is made up. They will not find me there," said Peter.

Mary was upset with emotional despair. "How will you get there? I'll take the children; we will run with you," Mary pleaded.

"Mary, you will not do anything. Germany wants me because I am a German. You have the money we withdrew from the bank before the war. There is the gold hidden in the shed. You can live comfortably from it. When it becomes too dangerous to stay here, go to your sister's village. I'll meet you there. Take care of Vladek and John for me. Now, I'm going to Charles. I have to get some things done in town," said Peter as he walked out in a hurry.

Mary tried to calm the children, who were in deep distress. John was two years old and Vladek three. Both of them did not understand the seriousness of the whole affair. They could only rely on their parents. When Peter came out of the home, the neighbors rushed in to ask, what was going on? Mary informed them the entire story, of the incident. "What will Peter do?" asked the worried neighbors.

"I do not know," said Mary. She did not want to reveal Peter's plan. People here lived like one big family, but, in these days of turmoil, Peter and Mary had to be very cautious.

Peter came late in the evening and was very tired. Mary was waiting for him with great impatience. "Where have you been, for so long?" asked Mary.

"I had to deal with a couple of things. Everything is taken care of. Charles will look after you," said Peter. Mary burst into tears. Peter was leaving her; she knew this. Peter, in all likelihood, would probably be shot, or arrested, for not signing the "Volksdeutsche" list. They both spoke about these things privately in a conversation for a long period and then Peter made the final decision. He would go to Mary's sister, Hanna's house to wait out the difficult moments, in anticipation of the full development of a dire situation.

Peter then pulled out his backpack from the upstairs closet and Mary gave him some food, for the road. "Mary...do not give me a lot. I will not be able to carry all of this. Leave it for you, and children," said Peter. In the evening, Peter then said goodbye, heartily with John, Vladek and Mary. They all cried. Peter came out of the kitchen and closed the door behind him.

Mary was now alone with the children. She sat down on the chair, embracing the children to herself, and said, "God, into your hands I give, Peter. Take care of me and the children. Amen."

Chapter II
Separation

PETER LEFT THE HOUSE WITH profound emotion in his heart. He thought about Mary and the children, all the time. He told himself, "I have to survive; I must survive. Everything will be fine. This war will end soon and I will see them again," Peter then thought to himself, not knowing whether the truth of events would be different. Peter traveled to the other side of town to meet with his good friend, Andrew Miller, who was also in a similar situation. Andrew chose not to sign the "Volksdeutsche" list as well. Miller was not yet married. The men walked all night to avoid German patrols.

Along the way, Andrew said to Peter, "If something should happen to me, everything is yours."

Peter was surprised by these words. He grabbed Andrew by the sleeve. Andrew then stopped, for a moment and Peter said, "I do not understand what you're saying."

"Maybe one day you will understand," said Andrew and moved on. In the morning, they arrived at their destination.

Mary arose early in the morning. She dressed John and Vladek, fed them and waited for the events of that day. Mary knew that the Gestapo would come early for the answer from Peter. How will they react to his absence? The Gestapo was no one to mess around with. They could arrest or kill anyone without a hesitation. There was a war and waiting was the worst feeling anyone could endure.

Approximately at nine o'clock in the morning, the same vehicle stopped in front of the house. Captain Shultz exited from his staff car, accompanied by two soldiers. Without knocking, Shultz entered the house. He found Mary sitting on a chair with her small children. At the sight of Shultz, Mary immediately rose from her chair, clutching John and Vladek. When Shultz saw only Mary and the children he asked, "Where is your husband, Peter Mayer; is he gone?"

"He went to the village for potatoes," answered Mary, who was frightened.

"Search the entire house," said Shultz, who gave orders to the soldiers who were with him. To Mary, he commanded, "You get out of this house." Mary exited the house with the children into the yard.

"There is no one at home," replied a nearby soldier.

"I'll ask you, one last time. Where is your husband?!" exclaimed Shultz.

"I told you, he went to the village for potatoes," said Mary surprised.

"You're lying... woman," Shultz shouted again. He swung at Mary's face. He wanted to violently hit Mary, however, Shultz stopped at the last moment. He checked his behavior and became greatly convicted and embarrassed when he saw the frightened children, clinging to their mother. "He escaped. But I'll find him!"

stammered Shultz as he pushed Mary, with great fury. Mary fell backwards. Crying with fear, she embraced her traumatized children. "Now, get out of here," denounced Shultz. Mary remained with the children, anxious and frightened in the yard.

Shultz said a direct command to one of the soldiers and walked toward the vehicle. A soldier fired a machine gun in the house. Bullets knocked out the glass of the windows and made holes in the wall, and door. A helmeted soldier then threw a grenade into the basement through a small window and ran quickly to the side. Mary saw what was happening, and turned her back, as a shield to protect her children. The force of the fragmentary grenade explosion knocked her and the children to the ground. The children's screams and cries echoed across the yard. The vibration and voluminous strength of the grenade explosion destroyed part of the wall in their home. When the grey dust cleared, Mary then saw a hole in their home. The Gestapo left in a hurry.

Nearby, the neighbors saw that the Gestapo left and they went out of their homes to comfort Mary. Friends wept with compassion for her. No one knew that Peter had indeed escaped. Mary explained the alarming situation, to her neighbors. "What are you going to do now?" asked her frightened neighbors.

"I have to somehow repair the wall because winter is coming," said Mary.

"We will surely help you," said her neighbors, witnessing the damage caused by the nearby grenade explosions.

In the afternoon, her cousin, Charles came to Mary. Mary informed him of the complete story of the Gestapo's visit. "Peter asked me to help you in everything. He went to the village to prepare provision for you and the children," said Charles. Mary and Charles comforted each other. After a while, he said, "It is late. I must go. I will come to you again in two days." Charles then walked away; in haste, to his home.

Peter and Andrew came to the village where Hanna lived. When Hanna saw Peter with the other man in the door; she sat down. The worst thoughts crept into her head. "Where's Mary?" asked Peter and Andrew. They sat down at the table and Hanna gave them food because they were both tired and hungry after an overnight walk. They both walked and traveled 30 miles. After a while, Adam, Hanna's husband, also learned about the unfolding experiences of Peter and Mary.

Peter continued to discuss everything. He said, "In time we will bring Mary here with the children."

Adam responded, "Somehow, we all will handle this difficult situation. There will be work in the field. We will harvest potatoes, beets, onions, and carrots for the winter. Your friend can stay here too."

"Thank you very much," said Peter.

"I also thank you," said Andrew.

"Now, we have to prepare the secret room and lodging for you and your family in the attic," said Adam. Everyone then got up from the table and walked away, determined, to realize the eventual plan.

Mary and her neighbors repaired the damage done by the grenade. The basement suffered the most. The hole in the wall was boarded up. They also cleaned up the basement. Mary with her children could now live peacefully, in their home which they built together with Peter three years earlier.

The Gestapo came twice on the premises and inquired about Peter. The situation became very serious and terrifying. A month passed, and on one quiet morning, the Gestapo car came again and stopped in front of every house on this quiet street, and provided in writing, that the residents of each house had twenty-four hours to vacate their property. The family could only take a few personal things. All furniture was discarded in the street; few items remained in the homes. These twelve houses were later occupied by the Germans.

There was a great commotion in the street. Crying was heard above the tops of the trees. Mary left John and Vladek with her neighbors. She then quickly went to Charles. Fortunately for Mary; he was at home. Mary explained the matter to him. Charles and Mary returned to her home. In the shed, he found a small carriage to which he had loaded their most important belongings. Mary relocated these items with her children into Charles' home. They drove to Charles' home which took approximately 30 minutes.

They unloaded small household items and left Vladek and John in the care of Charles' wife, Sophia. Together, they went back for the rest of the important things they could carry. It required four hours to empty out the things they needed from the house, such as the food they had collected for the winter. Mary did not forget to take the money from the secret place and the gold from the shed. Finally, she said her goodbyes to her neighbors. They didn't know if they would ever see each other again.

The Germans were violent in their retaliation to the Poles. Charles pulled the heavily loaded cart and tried to comfort Mary on the way home. The day passed without incident. They reached Charles' house and unloaded the small carriage. Charles and Mary entered into the kitchen where Sophie prepared dinner. After dinner, Mary laid her children down to sleep. Charles, Sophie, and Mary sat for a long time and contemplated what they should do next.

Peter was in the process of receiving a written message in code, hidden in ordinary appearing objects from Mary through Charles every week. He was disturbed by the news of Mary's move. Peter had hoped that Mary and his children would spend winter in their home with the preparations that were made. He was vigilant, hopeful and relieved that Mary had taken most of the necessary things.

Peter informed everyone about the incident with the grenade. He understood the consequence that a large number of people staying at Adam and Hanna's home might raise unnecessary suspicion. It was unknown who the informants in the village were. Peter could not carelessly jeopardize not only his family but also the family members of Adam and Hanna and their two children. The agreement was then made that Mary and her children would come there in two weeks. From the beginning of his escape from the city, Peter's plan was to wait out the winter and in the spring, his family would move to Olsztyn. There it was relatively quiet. Peter had a cousin there, Klaus Fisher, and he hoped to stay there longer, waiting for a better opportunity.

A few days passed with the desperate message that was delivered to Charles to prepare Mary and the children, to immediately leave the house. The appointed day came and at 9 am the old truck filled with coal halted in front of Charles' house. Charles and the driver loaded everything on the truck. Mary accompanied John and Vladek to the truck. The driver had a permit for the transport of coal to the village. Mary had prepared clever bribes, rolls of sausages for the Germans in a likelihood of patrols on the roads. Patrols from outposts were common, with no apparent order between major cities.

Halfway, a German patrol stopped them. There were two motorcycles and four Germans. "Your documents," said one of the Germans. The truck driver handed over his documents to the German patrol, with one permit to deliver the coal. The Germans checked over all the contents looking for contraband in the truck. The patrolman walked over to the driver and gave him the documents. "You!" said the German to Mary. She handed him her papers. The German looked at the document, and later, at the children and asked, "Where are you going?"

"I'm going to my sister. My home was destroyed and I have nowhere to live," said Mary. Obligingly, Mary handed the prepared bundle to the Germans. The Germans surveyed the paper documents and it was then that he saw a roll of sausage.

His face smiled. He grabbed the sausage and showed it to the others. Other Germans began to speak, "Sausage, sausage." Standing here for a long time, their breath and posture demonstrated that they were cold and hungry. The patrol handed over the documents to Mary and ordered them to continue to drive.

Peter continued to wait anxiously and then impatiently, for the arrival of Mary with their children. He had not seen them for nearly two months. Finally, the truck drove into the yard. Peter ran to the truck, opened the door, and helped Mary out of the truck together with their children.

He greeted them warmly, tenderly, and affectionately; he kissed Mary, John, and Vladek, and hugged them tightly. Mary greeted her sister Hanna, her husband Adam, and Andrew. Peter walked over to the driver and thanked him with great relief and consideration and handed him the agreed sum of money, for the favor. The driver quickly departed, to deliver coal to the address shown on the pass. They all went into the house, where Mary had told them of their experiences.

Chapter III
Tragedy

SEVEN DAYS PASSED. PETER ALONG with Andrew, continued to move in the direction of Olsztyn. This was to be a covert reconnaissance mission before he displaced his family to Olsztyn. Peter did not want to completely expose them to the risk of not knowing, whether or not his cousin continued to live at the old address. His cousin, before the war, had said something about moving to another city. Peter and Andrew had previously prepared documents. They were traders of construction materials. Both of them spoke German fluently which was helpful. The beginning of the journey went successfully. Peter knew the geographical area well having been in the general region many times on other related commercial matters.

Along the way, Peter and Andrew stopped in a small town near Olsztyn. There, they met a familiar acquaintance, a Pole, who was discouraged, telling them of dangers, not to go further. The Germans centrally searched the local villages for the dissident members of the resistance movement. "For now, it is quiet here, but for how long, no one really knows," said the Pole.

"There are only 20 miles left. I'm leaving early tomorrow, before sunrise. I have to ensure the safety of my family," said Peter.

"No. I insist, I'm coming with you," said Andrew.

"This is a very dangerous road. Stay here hidden, undercover until I get back," said Peter.

"No, I'm going with you! We came together, and we will go together to Olsztyn," said Andrew.

Very early in the morning, Peter and Andrew went on their way. They crisscrossed through the open fields and the forests to avoid the Germans with their many patrols. While standing in the middle of the road, they saw their objective in the distance, the small village. "I have a bad feeling about all of this. All night I could not sleep. Events are going to happen here," said Andrew.

"What do you mean?" asked Peter.

"I have this uncomfortable fear, I do not like this village," said Andrew. "We dare not, go through with it. We will walk around the village on the right side and will follow the banks of the forest." After about a half mile they noticed a truck approaching the village from the opposite side.

"It must be an offensive by the Germans. We need to run into the forest," said Andrew. They both ran for about three minutes breaking through trees and bushes. They heard shots being fired above their heads. The sound of machine guns and single shots disturbed birds and animals of the forest. The echoes came from all sides. Peter and Andrew stood frozen in total terror.

"Run to the right!" shouted Peter!

Crossing hastily through the woods, they noticed the ruins of a burned building. The sounds of the shots were getting steadily closer. "What are they doing here? The Germans, the patrols are everywhere," said Andrew, looking around carefully. After a moment, Andrew saw in the distance a shadow that resembled a dugout. They both came close to that place. It was actually a recessed dugout which led downward with stairs. Peter came cautiously in front of wooden doors and carefully pushed them.

A light illuminated from the interior. Peter walked in, looked around and noticed within the dugout that it consisted of two rooms. One larger room, full of empty crates and the second room opened with a small broken door. Peter leaned forward and found that there was only room for two people. He exited quickly from the dugout and said to Andrew, "There is a small storage space. We'll both fit in there."

Peter went into the dugout first, followed by Andrew. Peter first entered the small room and then Andrew. Andrew set up a stack of boxes to cover the entrance, so that the entrance would be hidden as much as possible. Secure from the inside, Andrew fixed something that resembled a small door and crouched down beside Peter. They both sat quietly, with bated breath. Nearby they heard continued gunshots.

From within the dugout, they heard thunderous shots from a machine gun with a few random shots. Two people fell into the dugout. Peter and Andrew heard someone who spoke Polish. One of the men said, "This is the end. They have us." After a moment, they heard German propaganda; speech, over the dugout.

One of the Germans shouted in broken Polish, "Give up. You are surrounded."

"What do we do?" asked one of the men in the dugout. "If we surrender, we will be submitted to torture, interrogation and then shot."

"What's the difference? Whether, we die now or later," said the second man. Then Peter heard the two men begin to pray, "Our Father, who art in heaven ..."

The German called out again, "Come out or die!" There was only terror. When both men finished the prayer, there was a loud crack, a series of machine gun fire. The wooden door was riddled with bullets, the door barely held on by its primitive hinges. One of the German soldiers threw a grenade into the dugout. A powerful explosion shook the dugout. The wall behind them shook and fell with a cloud of dust. The explosion threw them into the corner of the small room. Peter felt an overwhelming, stabbing pain and lost complete consciousness.

Upstairs there was a sound of movement by German soldiers. When the dust settled, the Nazis saw that they completely destroyed the dugout. A German officer was ordered to search the shattered dugout. One of the soldiers with a light carefully descended the stairs and searched the remains of the dugout. "I see two bodies. None are alive," said the soldier.

"For sure?" asked the officer.

"Yes," answered the soldier.

After a moment, the officer said, "We're going back."

Peter woke up. The sky was grey and overcast. Stillness reigned everywhere. Peter could not move and felt a terrible pain in his head and throughout his body. He raised his right hand and touched his face. He felt warm blood. "Andrew. Where is Andrew?" Peter thought. With a sore hand, he began to search for Andrew. Andrew lay beside him. He did not move. "Andrew. Andrew?" whispered Peter. Andrew did not answer. His body was limp. He could not tell if he was alive or not. Peter carefully pushed Andrew's body, aside. There was no light, it was dark. He began to touch something that reflected a beam.

He tensed and embraced the beam. Rays of light illuminated the place where they were. Andrew still lay motionless. Peter with the last of his strength began to push the boards and stones with earth out of his way to be able to free himself of the demolished remnants, of the dugout. Next, he spotted the bodies of two men. They were both dead. "They fought for the Homeland, for Poland," thought Peter. "They saved my life. Now, they lye in the motionless earth, dead, with their memories."

Peter struggled for about half an hour before he finally pulled Andrew out from the destroyed dugout. Peter laid him under the tree. After a few moments he witnessed Andrew breathing, he lived, but he was unconscious. Peter searched the remains of the dead bodies of the killed men. His search yielded convenient necessary items. Peter removed their jackets and covered their faces. The night was fast approaching. Barely walking, Peter brought many branches and made a place to sleep. "Tomorrow morning I will decide what to do next," Peter said to himself and fell asleep lying next to Andrew.

In the morning, Andrew woke him, mumbling. "He lives," said a sleepy Peter.

"What happened?" asked Andrew.

"The Germans threw a grenade into the dugout," said Peter.

"Where are the two men?" asked Andrew.

"They're dead," replied Peter and then he continued, "I pulled you out and we slept here all night. The most important thing is that you're alive."

Andrew was in great pain. He firmly grabbed Peter's arm and with a soft voice he simply said, "I do not think I'm going to get out of here."

"Be honest; do not make foolish jesting, it's all right. I'm confident you too will get out of this," said Peter.

"Listen to what I'm saying," Andrew grabbed Peter by the shirt. "I have a letter in my jacket. Everything will be yours," and at this moment on Andrew's face appeared a great grimace of pain. His chest rose up and quietly dropped. Andrew gave up his ghost.

"Andrew, Andrew," Peter began to cry out pulling on his body. Breathing ceased. Andrew was dead. Peter could not come to terms with the situation. He cried miserably that he had taken Andrew with him. "It's my entire fault. It's my fault," Peter said to himself.

Thirty minutes passed before Peter, in accordance with the wishes of Andrew, began to search his jacket. He found a wallet from which he withdrew money. The important documents and identification, he destroyed. Peter did not find any letter. He started again, searching the entire jacket; in desperation, he ripped the lining and sleeves. There was no letter. The last place he had not searched for was obvious, the collar. He began to touch the collar carefully. "There it is," said Peter. The letter was very cleverly inserted in the collar.

Finally, he removed and unfolded, the letter. Peter's heart started pounding. "Peter. We have been friends for a long time. I am just like you, a German; I grew up in Poland. As you know, my parents have passed away and I have no siblings. You were like a brother to me. I leave you everything I have. Look at the cemetery." There was a small hand-drawn map. Peter looked at it carefully; and destroyed the letter. Now, he remembered how Andrew at the beginning of his escape, had spoken to Peter exactly the same words, "If anything unfortunate should happen to me, everything is yours." Now, Peter understood the meaning of those words. Andrew already had apprehension about his life. Peter with great regret tore the letter into small pieces and buried it in the ground.

It was noon when Peter stood on the edge of the forest. Smoke ascended and hovered from a few burned buildings. "The Germans were here too," said Peter to himself. He stood for a moment; watching the village. Peter noticed an old man working around the building. He decided to take the risk; to approach him. Peter had to walk about 100 yards to see the house.

The man was busy from work in the barn. The sight of the approaching stranger created fear. He stood frightened. Peter was filthy, bloody and his clothes were a tattered, mess. "Good morning," said Peter. "I'm Peter. There are three bodies lying in the forest inside a burned building, two partisans and my friend Andrew. They died yesterday; from a grenade thrown by the Germans." Then Peter shared the facts of the whole event. The old man slowly began to trust him. He grabbed him by the arm and led Peter to his home.

When they entered a large room, there was an old woman busy around the stove. The sight of the stranger caused her to stop. "Do not be afraid. This is a Pole," the man said briefly telling the whole story. "Go to the neighbors and call Stanley." The woman threw a warm jacket on her back and left the house. The old man poured water into the bowl so that Peter could wash himself. After a few minutes, she returned with a tall man.

Here the old man introduced himself to Peter, "My name is Fred." Then the old man said, "This is Stanley, our friend, and our neighbor. You can trust him." Peter told him the entire history of the expedition.

"It would be decent, to bury them." Stanley said, "We'll do it," then they departed the room.

After a moment, the old man returned and invited Peter to the table to have something to eat. "This is my wife Anna," said the man. Peter finished eating, Anna bandaged Peter's wounds and led him into a small bedroom, where Peter lay on the bed and fell asleep quickly.

In the morning Peter was stiff, sore and bruised. When he entered the kitchen, Fred and Anna were sitting at the table. They also invited Peter to the table as they ate, a hot breakfast together. During breakfast, Fred spoke of what the Germans did to the village. "They only were looking for partisans. They looted and burned a few houses on the path. The men in the woods have all been taken care of. They are buried in the cemetery," said Fred.

"I want to thank you, very much for my friend Andrew. He was a good man," said Peter.

"What are you going to do now?" asked Fred.

"I have to think about it. I need to get to Olsztyn," said Peter.

"You can stay here as long as you require, until you feel better. In four days our neighbor goes to Olsztyn. He can take you there. It is all arranged. Think about whether you want to go with him," said Fred.

Chapter IV
Decision

FOUR DAYS PASSED, AND PETER felt slightly better. During this time, his days were spent in seclusion and bed rest. His conscience thought a lot. Peter knew that in the countryside Mary was with their children, they could not remain unattended. He decided to continue the journey directly north, in haste, to Olsztyn to find his cousin Klaus. Breakfast finished, Peter now was ready to travel. Several minutes passed and a truck arrived loaded with timber. Peter thanked Fred and Anna for their care. He climbed into the truck. Before he closed the door he said, "Let's see each other again, soon my friend."

The truck crept forward moving slowly. They rode on the bumpy road that led to Olsztyn. On the outskirts of the town, Peter saw a sight that brought only mistrust. A German occupation patrol, "Documents," said one of the Germans. The driver handed him the documents. The German sternly looked around the vehicle. He carefully checked the load and handed the driver's documents back to him. Then he reached for Peter's papers. He looked Peter directly in the eye and asked, "You are German. Do you speak the language?"

Peter was surprised, he replied, "Yes."

"What are you doing here?" asked the German.

"I'm going to my cousin who lives in Olsztyn." The German looked at Peter, gave him the documents, and ordered them to go on. Peter breathed a sigh of relief. The truck drove up to the indicated address. Peter thanked the driver for the quick ride and the departure.

The truck rumbled off. Peter stood in front of the neatly-kept home. He opened the gate and entered the yard. He knocked on the door. After a moment, the door opened. A tall, broad-shouldered man filled the doorway. "Peter! What are you doing here?" asked his cousin Klaus. He greeted Peter warmly.

"It's a long story; I will tell you about it," said Peter and they both went inside. Klaus ran a small business, dealing with the cutting down of trees in the forests.

"Gertrude went to town for a shopping trip. She will return within an hour. Would you like some coffee?" asked Klaus.

"Yes," replied Peter. Klaus made coffee and they both sat down at the table.

"You're fortunate that I was at home. I did a minor settlement. Now tell me, what brought you here?" asked Klaus, impatiently. Peter began to tell him the details about the account. When Peter finished, Klaus said, "I see that you have had a very difficult situation". After a long pause, he asked "What are you going to do next?"

Peter looked at Klaus and said, "Tell me, can we live with you?"

Klaus, surprised, looked at Peter and said, "There is plenty of space in my home."

Peter replied. "Can you do it? Will you manage it?"

"When Gertrude comes we will discuss the important details. What will happen when the Germans stop you? They will be asking about your business and your identity pass. You will be arrested," said Klaus. Peter and Klaus began to talk about how to avoid it.

"I have money," said Peter.

"I know someone who can help you," said Klaus. "First we will wait patiently for Gertrude."

Exactly an hour passed before Gertrude returned from shopping. She was very elated, to see her cousin. Peter had to tell his story, once again. "I'm glad we will be together again," said Gertrude.

"For now all is quiet here, but you do not know how it will be tomorrow," said Klaus. "Now, we will both go to the city to get paperwork" They both left the house. They walked cautiously, watching on all sides. The Germans endlessly patrolled the city and often did random inspections.

Klaus and Peter arrived at the brick building on the outskirts of the city. "Wait here," said Klaus to Peter as he carefully walked inside the house himself. After five minutes, Klaus came out and said, "Come on. He will help you, but it will cost a little money."

Peter replied, "Just see to it that he is paid, what he does he does quickly," and they both went in.

A friend of Klaus took a photo of Peter and said, "Come tomorrow afternoon it will be ready." Peter gave the agreed sum of money; for the complete execution of documents, that were agreed as promised.

The next day, Klaus received the necessary documents for Peter. Peter spent two days with his cousin. Klaus prepared the select documents and notarized them for Peter, a fictitious contract to deliver wood, in the event that problems might arise. Now is the time of parting to say the expected goodbyes. Gertrude said to Peter, "Come again as soon as possible. It will be safer here than in the countryside. We'll be waiting for you." They all said their goodbyes. Peter went back to Mary and their children.

Two weeks slowly passed, since the time when Peter left with Andrew. Mary was restless. Endless turmoil tormented her thoughts. They bombarded her mind. She thought, "What has happened to them? What if they do not come back? What if they don't come back after a week? What will I do as a widow; when Peter does not return home? The Children are small and we do not have a home. I'll be completely alone." She was continually tortured with those thoughts. "Everything will be fine. Peter will be back at home soon. Nothing has happened to them," she said to herself, "I worry too much."

Late in the evening, Adam, Hanna, and Mary sat at the kitchen table. There was a loud knocking on the door. "Who can that be?" asked Hanna. Adam arose and went out into the hall, and continued walking to the closed door. He asked, "Who's there?"

"It's me, Peter." Adam quickly turned the key in the lock and opened the door. Peter came inside. Adam closed the door and both of them greeted each other warmly, with affection.

"Where's Andrew?" asked Adam.

"He's dead," said Peter. Together they entered the kitchen. Mary jumped to her feet and ran to Peter. Peter embraced Mary, who was inconsolable. She was overcome with emotion. They stood there for, about a minute.

Finally, Hanna approached Peter and greeted him asking, "Where's Andrew?"

Peter said with a firm voice, "He's dead."

"Oh. No! That's not possible. How could this happen?" asked Mary.

"Let me tell you the story; first tell me; how are the children?"

"Healthy. They are sleeping now. They could not wait to see their Father," said Mary. Peter was relieved with this message. He longed for John and Vladek.

"Change your clothes and wash up. I'm going to prepare us something to eat," said Hanna.

Fifteen minutes later, everyone was sitting at the table drinking hot tea. Peter ate dinner. He began to tell the story of his journey. They all cried after the loss of Andrew. He was a good friend. "It's late and now it's time to rest. Let's go to sleep and tomorrow we'll talk," said Adam. Hanna and Adam went to bed. Peter and Mary reflected for a while in conversation before heading off to their bedroom. In the bed next to Mary and Peter, slept John and Vladek. Peter was so tired, fell asleep instantly. Mary clinging to him could not sleep. She laid awake a long time considering the situation. Finally, she fell into an exhausted sleep.

Peter arose early in the morning and ignited the stove. He boiled the water for the coffee. One hour later, everyone was sitting at the table. They ate breakfast. Peter could not wait to see his children. Eight o'clock in the morning the children were awake. They went to the kitchen and Vladek saw Peter. "Father," he shouted as he ran to him, throwing himself into the arms of Peter. John also ran to Peter. Everyone enjoyed the humor and presence of Peter. Throughout the day, Vladek and John did not leave the sight of their father nor did they take a step away from his approval. In the evening, Peter went to bed with the boys. They did not want to go to sleep without their father.

There was a suspicious man in the village. The stranger inquired if there was a new man in the village. Everyone knew each other but in these difficult times, anything was possible. The situation was becoming increasingly dangerous. Peter and Mary challenged themselves to decide the best way to handle the situation. They did not have another option. They did not want to expose Adam and Hanna to danger. The only reasonable option was to go to Olsztyn. Hanna was emotional and upset that Mary was leaving. It was very traumatic for her to part with her sister. She understood the seriousness of the situation. Peter posted a letter to his cousin that they were arriving next week approximately, Thursday afternoon. The mail was strictly monitored and controlled by the Germans. Peter was very cautious coding what he wrote.

Chapter V
Relocation

ETER INFORMED CHARLES ABOUT the decision he had made with Mary. A few days passed, Charles sent a truck to take Mary with the children back to the city. The appointed time came for parting. Mary and the children said goodbye to her sister, Hanna. Peter could not go with them. He had to be especially careful. He was marked by the Gestapo. Three days later Mary with John and Vladek boarded the train going to Olsztyn. Mary was well aware that she must inevitably rely only on herself. Vladek asked Mary, "Where is father?" Mary explained to him that his father was working in Olsztyn and now they're going to him.

The train left the station. After about half an hour he departed at the first train station where a few people got off and a few people entered the train. Mary did not know how Peter had decided to travel to Olsztyn. Peter did not want to unjustly expose Mary to the danger of telling her how critical errors create a catastrophe. Very bad things can happen to good people. This trip was certainly dangerous for both Peter and Mary.

The conductor began to check the tickets. Behind him, two Germans verified their identity with cards and other necessary documents. The door slid open to the compartment and vibrated from side to side and one of the Germans said in his natural dialect, "Documents please." There were six other people in the compartment. Those on board obediently gave them their documents. Mary sat with her children looking out the window enjoying the scenery. The country is especially beautiful this time of the year. She held out her hand with the documents. The German opened the document; looked at Mary and the children and asked, "Where are you going?"

"To Olsztyn. To my cousin," Mary replied in German. She knew German, very well.

"Why are you going there?" he asked again.

"It's a birthday celebration and Holiday," replied Mary. The German turned to his colleague and exchanged a few words with him quietly. Fear gripped Mary, but she dare not show it. It would be a sign of weakness and not following a direct order officially. She tried to smile politely to the Germans.

The German turned and said, "Somewhere I have heard your name, but I cannot remember where?"

Behind the conductor, the Gestapo agent said, "Watch the children," he smiled at Mary and handed her the papers.

"I will keep a close eye on the lovely little ones," said Mary. Then the German conductor smiled and closed the door in the compartment. Mary then sighed with great relief.

The conductor and the Gestapo continued to inspect and control documents through their notebooks and notations. They went on to the next car and opened the first compartment. There were three men sitting there. "Documents please?" said the Gestapo. A man in a black hat and a shiny leather coat handed over his documents. The German looked at the document, it showed the name, "Peter Weiss." The German looked again at the man in the leather coat and said, "Thank you," handing him the documents and at the same time wondering, "Who can this be? He certainly looks like the Gestapo." After checking the other two men's documents the Gestapo closed the door of the compartment. The man in the leather coat breathed a sigh of relief. Staying in the chamber he waited tentatively in the coach for about five minutes, stood up and exited into the corridor from the carriage.

The man looked around to see where the Germans were. They checked the next compartments. The man in the leather coat went to the next coach. He walked deliberately and slowly. He raised his collar upward and slides his hat forward above his eyes. The man passed by the compartment where Mary sat with her children several times and glanced furtively at the compartment. Mary embraced the children to herself. They all looked at the reflection of the scenery.

The train stopped at several stations on its journey. There were German patrols surveying at regular intervals. Finally, the train reached Olsztyn. Mary with John and Valdek got off the train and headed quickly for the waiting room. At a safe distance, they were followed by the man in the leather coat. He walked confidently. At the window of the coach, the man in the leather coat noticed two Germans who were checking the documents on the train. He looked at them with his stony face, nodded to them and went on. They looked for him until he disappeared behind the corner of the building. They had a suspicion he was following someone. They did not know whom. The train continued on its way and they went about their business. The Gestapo saw the stony-faced man again as he walked slowly towards downtown.

Mary approached the waiting room and looked around nervously. Against the wall near the door, she noticed Klaus standing, who quickly went to her, and greeted her and the children warmly. Mary held John and Vladek by the hand and Klaus took two suitcases and they left the building. They walked to the car. Klaus opened the door and Mary went inside with her children. Klaus put their suitcases in the trunk and closed it. Klaus sat down behind the wheel took a deep breath and slowly drove toward his house.

Klaus pulled into the yard. Mary got out of the car. At that moment, Gertrude opened the front door of the house and walked over to Mary. The last time they saw each other was when John was born. It was almost two years ago. They embraced each other and began to laugh and sob from the stress. Klaus pulled the suitcases out of the car and they all went into the house. Gertrude invited everyone to the table and served hot tea and black coffee that she had prepared earlier. "Warm up briefly and then I will serve dinner. Now tell us; how was your travel?" asked Gertrude, knowing that Peter had not come with Mary and their children.

A curious tall pale man in a leather coat was approaching the house where Klaus lives. He entered the gate into the yard and knocked on the door. "Who can it be?" asked Gertrude, who was frightened.

"Do not be afraid. It's your own." said Klaus, who did not want to pressure the facts. He stood up from the chair walked out into the corridor and slowly unlatched the lock opening the door.

"Come on, they are here," said Klaus.

"I know," the man in the shadow replied. He took off his hat, removed his coat and walked into the kitchen. Mary at the sight of the man, jumped from her chair and ran to Peter, and embraced him warmly. John and Vladek ran to him as well. "Father! Father!" shouted Vladek joyfully. Peter tightly held both of them lifting them with his hands and kissing and embracing them tenderly. This moment of tenderness lasted a few minutes.

After a moment Mary asked, "How did you come here?"

"On the same train, as you," said Peter.

"You rode on the same train as us?" asked Mary, who was surprised. "There were Gestapo agents there," said Mary.

"I know. I had to take precautions so that I would not be recognized. The Gestapo is clever, but I am shrewd. I boarded on the next station and rode in the second car," answered Peter. He then calmly walked out of the kitchen. He came back wearing a leather coat and a black hat. "Do you like the disguise?" asked Peter.

"Did you walk in the corridor in the train car and look into our compartment?" asked Mary.

"Yes. It was me," replied Peter.

"I saw your back twice in the corridor, but I thought it was more Gestapo. You were not afraid of the Gestapo; who diligently checked the documents?" Mary asked.

"I was terrified. But they did not know who I am. I had the name Weiss. I was dressed like them. I was in disguise with a leather coat and black hat," said Peter. "I could not leave you alone with the children." Here Mary burst into happy tears and began to tenderly kiss Peter's face. They all sat down at the table and began to eat the dinner Gertrude had prepared.

Chapter VI
Klaus' Arrest

I T WAS ALREADY WINTER. THE SNOW covered the ground with a thick layer of white. In the office of headquarters sat, dutifully; Captain Schultz. Shultz picked up the phone and said, "Call Sergeant Knapp."

A few minutes later sergeant Knapp came in with a snap of his shoes and said, "Heil Hitler".

"Sit down," Shultz said. "I read your report. Approximately two weeks ago on the train to Olsztyn, you met a woman named Mayer."

"Yes, sir," said Knapp.

"Tell me more about this incident," said Shultz.

Knapp began to relate the story, "She was in the compartment with two children. Sitting in the office I opened the document and immediately saw the name Mayer, it was obvious to me as I remembered that I saw in the morning papers, current dissidents. The woman in question spoke German rather well and was not behaving suspiciously. I asked my duty officer who was with me if he recognized her, but this particular name meant nothing to him. By checking the reports yesterday, I was alerted by Mayer's name. He is wanted by this office of the Gestapo. I remember an unknown man dressed officially like us, in a leather coat. He had German identification and names. I observed he was one of us. I did not ask him any questions. I saw him again on the train as he walked in the coach corridor, but not in his car only in another. It seemed to me that he followed the woman with two small children who got off the train. As we stood on the platform, our eyes met as he passed by us. He bowed his head before us and we moved on. The train departed, I saw him again leaning on the corner of the train department building searching for people."

"What did he look like; someone on another agenda?" asked Shultz.

"Tall, Aryan, dark-haired, broad-shouldered. Typical German," replied Knapp.

"That's him, Peter Mayer; the husband of the suspect. I was in his house. I urged him to cooperate with us, to no avail. He ran away. All of it is to be searched. Surely, he is somewhere in Olsztyn," said Shultz.

"I remember the young woman said that she was going to her cousin," said Knapp.

"Very efficient. Well done Knapp, you're awake. I commend you, tomorrow, you will go to Olsztyn. I will prepare the paperwork; all that is necessary; all documents will be notarized and stamped to arrest him. You are authorized to bring him here. You may now go away to your orders Knapp," said Shultz. Knapp stood up, saluted and went out.

Klaus with Peter ran a small logging company. Mary and the children adapted to the new conditions. Germany controlled the whole land of Poland. Their violence became a fear on an unprecedented scale. It was snowy and cold. Mary and the children practically did not go out anywhere; so as not to raise the suspicion of their neighbors. All eyes were alerted. Mouths were quick to speak. It was not clear who the enemies were and to whom they were serving and where their allegiance resided.

One day, Klaus was at the office of the city and he took care of the notarized papers he needed with great care so that no detail was overlooked. He had some good friends there. One of them Alfred Schmidt, approached Klaus and asked him to come to his office. They entered the office. Schmidt put his finger on his mouth and told Klaus to keep quiet. He went to Klaus and whispered in his ear, "The Gestapo is asking about you today. They have many questions for you." Klaus stiffened. "They also asked about some person named, Mayer," said Schmidt.

"Thank you, sir. I am grateful for this very important and truthful information," said Klaus and he quickly left the office.

Klaus was both stunned and surprised. He quickly drove home. When he came home he was pale as a painted wall. Gertrude thought that Klaus had a heart attack. "Tomorrow surely, the Gestapo will arrive. I do not know how this happened. They know that you're here," said Klaus looking at Mary.

"Oh. No!" said Mary. "Where is Peter?" asked Mary, who was horrified.

"Pack your things quickly. I'm going after Peter; into the woods. You have to run as fast as possible," said Klaus. He then quickly left the house.

Mary stayed at home with Gertrude and the children. "What will happen to us now?" asked Mary weeping.

"We'll think of something. I'll get the suitcases," said Gertrude and she left the kitchen. Mary entered the room where John and Vladek were playing and they embraced each other.

"Children you must listen. We're going on a journey. We need to run away from here," Mary whispered quietly. Gertrude brought from the attic two suitcases. Weeping she again packed only the most necessary things. Before Klaus and Peter arrived home, Mary was packed, prepared and ready for departure.

Peter and Klaus arrived home. Peter looked at Mary and said, "I am very sorry for what you are going through, but now; we have to get out of here."

"Where?" asked Mary.

"Abroad. I do not know yet exactly. Everything is being prepared." Wasting no time, Peter and Mary said their goodbyes to Gertrude.

Gertrude embraced Mary affectionately and kissed little John and Vladek and she said, "May God keep you in his care. In the stillness of the night, an angel will speak, to you all." Klaus delivered them to an agreed place. There was a coachman in a carriage, with two horses, who waited on them. "Where are we going?" Mary asked.

"Far away, to another place," answered Peter.

Klaus kissed the children, and then said goodbye, to Mary and Peter. "Be careful; I do not know what is waiting for us, but I promise you that I will not say anything about the secrets, for the safety of the children," said Klaus. The coach with the entire Mayer family moved slowly, forward.

Klaus did not sleep well at night knowing what he would expect in the morning. Gertrude already knew what to say, when the Gestapo arrived. Exactly at eight o'clock in the morning, two German staff cars stopped in front of the Klaus house. From one car exited two soldiers and the second Sergeant Knapp followed the driver. Knapp went to the door and pounded on it, saying, "Open the door, Gestapo!"

Klaus stood in the hallway and waited for them. He opened the door. "Where is Peter Mayer?" said Knapp, pushing Klaus into the hallway where Gertrude stood. "Search the house and the shed," he issued orders to the soldiers. Turning to Klaus, Knapp asked, "Where is Peter Mayer?" Klaus was frightened and pale as a ghost.

"Peter left yesterday," said Klaus. Knapp looked at him and hit him in the face with all his strength. Klaus swayed and staggered.

The blood poured from his nose and mouth. Once again he asked, "Where's Peter Mayer?" screamed Knapp!

"He is not here. He left yesterday with his family. He said he was going to Tczew," said Klaus.

Knapp looked at Gertrude and walked over to her, grabbing her by the hair until Gertrude cried out in pain, "You also do not know where he went?" asked Knapp

"I do not know," said Gertrude weeping.

"There's nobody here," said the soldier to the sergeant.

"Take him into custody and leave her," was the strict order issued by Knapp. They left the house with Klaus wearing only a sweater. He was pushed into the car. Gertrude stood and cried while looking at the departing staff car with Klaus in it.

When they arrived at the Gestapo Command Headquarters, they threw Klaus into a prison cell. There were already two other tortured prisoners covered with blood. They were all very quiet and they didn't say a word. Everyone was sitting in complete silence. After an hour, the door opened and a big German man grabbed Klaus and led him out of the cell. He led him to the room where sergeant Knapp was waiting for him. The sergeant sat behind a small desk. In the middle of the room there was a chair. The heavy door was closed. Klaus said to himself, "God keep me in your care."

Knapp asked Klaus, "Where is Peter Mayer."

"I do not know. He was with us for two weeks. Yesterday he said he was going to Tczew," said Klaus. Knapp's fist rocked Klaus' jaw; he felt a powerful blow to the face. Immediately Klaus was covered with spewed blood.

The sergeant looked at the papers and said, "I see you're German. It is not nice to lie." Klaus again got a second powerful blow to the head, this time on the other side. "That will help your memory," said Knapp. From that moment on Klaus could not remember anything. The brain fog dulled his senses; the trauma took him in and out of consciousness.

Klaus woke up in a cold damp cell. He was beaten, sore and bloody. Klaus sat down with great difficulty and stared at the reality of a barred little window. It was already dark. "I hadn't slept in a long time. They fixed me good," said Klaus in a low voice. Sitting in the cell, he reflected on what had happened. From the second strike, Klaus did not remember anything. "Did I tell them something?" wondered Klaus. I promised Peter that I would not say anything. Night came and darkness came with it. Klaus with regrets, pain, and fatigue fell asleep. The ghosts in the cell fell asleep with Klaus. They too slept well.

Morning came and the same German entered the cell. Klaus was lying down and could not get up. "Get up," said the German and grabbed Klaus by his sweater pulling him up to stand on his feet. Klaus barely stood on them. The German pushed Klaus forward. They entered the same room. Knapp sat at his desk. Klaus stood in front of him on his swollen rubbery feet. "Give him a chair," said Knapp to the German standing next to him, who automatically held the chair for Klaus. Klaus sat down heavily with relief. "And what? Have you considered the whole thing? Are you now willing to change your story?" asked Knapp.

Klaus looked at him and realized that he did not lose his tongue. "I do not remember anything. What would you like me to say?" asked Klaus.

The soldier standing next to Klaus tried to hit him but the sergeant stopped him raising his hand up and said, "Klaus, you have to tell us where Peter Mayer is, or you will go to the penal colony."

At these words, Klaus' eyes widened. He thought a moment and said, "I am an honest simple German. I told you what I know. It's not my fault that he came to me. I did not know that he was wanted by you."

"You're like a dog," Knapp shouted and the German standing next to Klaus hit him with all his strength and Klaus fell to the floor. "We're done. Send him to the penitentiary!" said Sergeant Knapp.

It was early afternoon when the wagon carrying Peter, Mary, John, and Vladek stopped in front of a modest house. They were traveling for almost the entire day. Everyone went inside the house. The house was empty. Tired, cold and exhausted they barely stood on their feet. The driver filled the stove with wood and lit it. After a few minutes, the home became warm in the living area. "I'm going to take the horses to the stable. I'll be back," said the coachman and he left the house.

Mary added the coal to the iron stove and finally established continuous warmth. Mary's family sat gathered around the hot stove, warming their hands. John and Vladek sat with Mary. Mary looked at Peter with tears in her eyes as if asking, "What is going to happen next?"

Peter understood her thoughts and said, "Everything will be fine." They sat silently until the old man arrived.

The coachman pulled off his old worn out jacket and hung it on the door and said, "I live alone. My name is Ted. My wife passed away last year. Well, it is good that she is not here to see these hard times. You're hungry; let me give you hospitality and something to eat." After a few minutes bread, eggs, butter, and milk appeared on the table. "Eat my friends, because certainly, the children are hungry. I will boil water for tea. I have a little honey from my hives. Perhaps it will sweeten your rough day," said Ted. John and Vladek ate bread with butter and were drinking milk.

Mary and Peter looked at them with joy after a difficult journey. The children have such an appetite! Immediately, after dinner, the children went to sleep in beds, which were in the corners of the room behind a small compartment. Peter, Mary, and Ted sat for a long time talking about the whole situation. Near midnight, Ted went to another room to sleep and Mary stayed with Peter in the kitchen. Peter added more coal to the furnace and stove and put two blankets on the floor. The couple laid on them. Intimately, warming each other. Tired, they fell asleep.

When Gertrude learned of the decision of the Gestapo, feeling helpless and damned she cried out in despair. She concluded she did not know what to do. Should she go to the Gestapo and tell everything she knows? Or was she to remain silent obeying what Klaus had said? Gertrude went through mental anguish. Finally, Gertrude decided to be completely silent. "Maybe all this will be for a short season. The war is almost finished. There will be peace in Russia. They will soon let him go," thought Gertrude, who was bewildered. She clearly understood conditions Mary suffered in private when she was alone.

Three days passed. Klaus was transported close to the truce line with Russia. All prisoners in the camp lived in wooden barracks. There were twenty-eight prisoners in this barrack where Klaus was staying. Wooden bunks stood in the barracks. In the middle, stood a small iron stove. It burned through the night attended only by one lone, grim, prisoner on duty. The prisoners were sent here for some offense. Select prisoners like Klaus numbered about a hundred in the camp, living in four barracks. The commander lived in better-insulated accommodations with new windows, stoves, and floors. Prisoners were undergoing training every day. At the end of the day, they barely walked. Winter was militant, heavy and frosty. Not all prisoners were able to withstand starvation; there were hardships of plagues, heavy exercises, and a host of cholera, and other diseases. Several died of exhaustion and from frostbite.

Four months passed. The command was given with an immediate order to expand the camp. For this task, they needed trained personnel acquainted with the construction of barracks. They decided to recruit labor from among the surviving prisoners. After checking all the files they made the final selection, seven soldiers who were physically capable of building new barracks. Among them was Klaus because he knew the German language and in the past was associated as a lumberman with a small company cutting down trees in the forest. Klaus was to be strictly controlled by Major Hase who had been sent to oversee the construction of twenty more efficient barracks. They had six months to modify prisoner accommodations. The order came straight from Berlin.

Klaus showed his good side in front of his superior Major Hase. He worked endlessly, to perform every command of his superior. A month passed and Klaus was moved to better accommodations. He had a small room with an iron stove, where he could sleep on a comfortable bed. Time passed quickly. The assignment that was given to Klaus was to prepare the ground for the construction. The prisoners worked long hours. The first working assignment was to fence in the open area and then the prisoners built the first of two additional barracks. In addition, fifty prisoners were sent to speed the completion of construction. Klaus had unlimited freedom in making decisions. The commander of the camp with Major Hase had complete trust in Klaus. Slowly each day passed. Everything was going as planned.

A month before the deadline, the barracks were built. Everyone admired the professionalism of Klaus.

Chapter VII
In the Escape East; the Near East

ETER, MARY, AND TED AROSE, early in the morning. Ted put the wood in the stove to get the house warm; before the children awoke. He made coffee and eggs and sat down at the table, together with Peter and Mary. They talked quietly. The children were still asleep. Finally, Ted said, "Give me your papers."

Peter understood what was happening, but Mary stiffened and asked, "Why… for what purpose?"

"Give him the papers and do not ask," said Peter. He handed over the important documents. Mary did the same.

"I'll return in three days. No one will know you're here," said Ted. Peter realized what Ted was about to do. Everything was arranged. They were still in Olsztyn. Klaus did not want to know where Ted sent Peter and his family to be settled. After an hour, Ted drove away. Peter, Mary, and the children were alone in the safe house. The cottage stood in quiet seclusion on the edge of a small village. A fine snow was falling in the stillness of the day.

Ted was an honest man who liked to do business with Klaus. They made money together. Work was steady, consistent and profitable. Despite the fact that Ted was the driver, he had many contacts within the city. Ted went out to create a new identity with newly created border documents for Peter and Mary. Peter's family knew they could not stay long at Ted's place.

The current times were very dangerous. The Germans controlled most of the borders of Poland. The Russians occupied the eastern territories of Poland. Poland; officially to the world did not exist. There was no future or a caring perspective, within view of the world and its liberation. At least at the present time with no end in sight of the current world.

Peter and Mary sat looking out the curtained windows of the house. They waited for three days patiently without going anywhere. The neighbors understood that Ted, from time to time, would come to see if everything was secure with the house. Ted's friends would drop by for a few days to spend time in the countryside. Families here lived well with each other. Although they witnessed the black smoke escaping from the chimney; no one paid any attention. In these hard times, people only thought about themselves. The turmoil and problems of everyone else were far away in the distance.

The third day came. Peter and Mary searched through the windows looking to see if Ted could be seen coming from far away. It was evening, and in the stillness of the night, Ted did not come. They both sat by the warm light of the candle. Night continued and Mary asked, "What shall we do if he does not arrive tomorrow? We don't have any of the necessary documents." She said, as she began to panic.

"I believe Ted will come. I know that it's risky; however, we have no other choice but to wait and try to be patient. We are on the blacklist with the Gestapo. Do you think that it is easy for me to live like this? What should I do? Give in and sign the "Volksdeutsche" list thus betraying all? How many people will be killed by my act? How many more have to die," Peter said irritably and continued, "Let's give him time, tomorrow… until noon."

"What will happen if he is delayed?" asked Mary, who was frightened.

"We will have to decide all of this, tomorrow," replied Peter, who spoke in a calm voice. It was now midnight. Mary and Peter lay down in restless sleep.

Peter arose early in the morning. He made a fire in the stove, boiled water and make black coffee and eggs. He waited until Mary was awake. Peter stared at her and admired her perseverance. When they got married, he promised her a peaceful, tranquil life. They could live in Germany; near Munich where his family originated instead, they chose Poland.

In Germany, Hitler came to the forefront of the world stage. He had extreme views. The people were optimistic, until the outbreak of war. If the family moved to Germany, Peter by now would surely have been in the army. Peter, with committed resolve, would take care of them in order to survive these difficult times. Everyone quietly said that this is not the end of the German expansion. Poles hoped that England and France would enter to help Poland. The help did not come. Here and there, resistance increased. The Nazis rushed in with fervent enthusiasm to suppress them.

Ten in the morning came; Ted finally arrived at the house tired. He covered himself in an old sheepskin coat and sat down at the table. He addressed Peter and Mary calmly, "There was a blockade just behind Olsztyn. There were several skirmishes; small groups had attacked the Germans on the road. They killed a few Nazis. The Germans retaliated by initiating a raid in the forest but they did not find anyone. In retribution, they steadily burned buildings in the village that were near the forest. It required an additional day to return home."

He put a cup of hot coffee to his mouth, burning him slightly as he slowly drank it. Peter and Mary stared at him, impatiently. Slowly he put the mug on the table and reached into his trouser pocket. He pulled out two new documents. "Now, you are Peter and Mary Krause. You were born in Germany, in the city of Munich. Here are your passes for free movement only in this area, if you are checked. May God keep you in the palm of His hand," said Ted who then handed them their documents.

Peter understood that his or Mary's names could not be changed or altered at the last minute on verifiable documents concerning John and Vlodek. They are used to their names. John had not spoken yet and Vlodek was only beginning to talk. It would be far easier to teach them to call themselves Krause. This was to be the role of Mary. They agreed with Ted that they would leave the following morning.

They would head to Russian controlled Lithuania; it gave its citizens freedom of action, but for how long? Only God knew. Peter did not want to run away to a land he did not know. These territories, cities, and land were very familiar. He has conducted business with many people in Poland, Lithuania and in East Prussia. Here he felt at home. Peter wanted to protect his family from the devastation and turmoil of the war.

Peter had the money, revenue, and gold which allowed him to survive this difficult season. The safety of his family was most important to him. The next day, Ted drove Peter with his family to a nearby town. There they stopped at a close friend of Ted's. Peter and Mary said goodbye to Ted. "May we meet again," said Ted. After their goodbyes, he headed to their province, uncertain of tomorrow, yet committed to his convictions.

In three more days Peter and his family arrived at their destination. Ted's friend Frederic welcomed them with joy and complete disbelief. Frederic lived alone. When the war broke out, his wife left him and went to Germany. Mary was tired and went to sleep with her children. Frederic and Peter sat for a long time telling each other their adventures. At the end, Frederic said, "Now there are too many Germans. Others claim that Hitler will want to go further to the East. I tell you, this will surely be a severe catastrophe. Tomorrow, I'll get a simple laborers job for you in my uncle's factory. Now we shall sleep. It is late."

Frederic arose early in the morning and went to his uncle's factory. In private he told uncle Horst the whole story. "Do you trust him?" asked Horst.

"Yes. I do. We have a tested relationship for ten years. We did continuous business together," said Frederic.

"Well, bring him in tomorrow to work, at seven. I have considerable work for him," said Horst and left the office. Frederic returned to the house and related the good news to Peter.

The village, where Peter was currently living, lay 30 miles from the border of Lithuania. Peter worked at Frederic's Uncle Horst's small factory, which sewed clothing. 30 people worked in the factory. Germany intermittently checked the identity of the workers in the factory. It was not their first priority. Days passed and finally months. Mary cared for her sons John and Vladek. She taught them social skills and to speak in Polish and German.

The Germans needed young men to join the army. Their recruitment of Germans was vital to their mission. Thanks to his Uncle's friends, Frederic and Peter remained safe. For how long, no one knew. The Germans were unpredictable and desired numbers of draft-eligible aged men. Their desire was to recruit Frederic and Peter into the army. Hurst explained to the authorities of the city that he needed young men to run the factory. Horst was now old and could not handle production on a daily basis to make a reasonable profit margin. The factory was operating at full capacity during this season for the German army.

Chapter VIII
Departure to Lithuania

I T WAS NOW APRIL 1940. Horst suggested to Peter and Fredric to travel immediately to Lithuania. They had to bring exported materials from the homeland which was much cheaper than contraband from Germany. Frederic and Peter looked at each other. They did not have to speak their intentions to each other and had an abiding trust. They understood what must be done. "We're going," said Frederic.

"You have to be very careful," said Horst. "Tomorrow I'll give you the important necessary documents."

Two days later, Frederic and Peter drove to the border of Lithuania. The Germans stopped them at the last checkpoint before Lithuania. They crossed the border surprisingly without difficulty; after they showed the correct papers. After 20 miles they were at the appointed destination. Peter spoke to the owner of the company, Lukas. Frederic and Peter paid cash for the goods they had loaded onto their truck. As usual, after the finalization of the transaction, the owner pulled out a bottle of vodka and obliged them to drink a few shots. They agreed that in two weeks they would be back for another three skids of material. They also spoke in conversation about the situation in Lithuania. After an hour of conversation, Frederic and Peter headed home.

Lithuanians on the border received a bottle of good vodka and were delighted to oblige them without problems. The Germans later in notarization of crossing, more diligently checked the documents and contents of their truck. The circumstance was verified. The Germans gave a sign at the checkpoint that they could go further.

After an hour, Frederic and Peter were in the factory. Uncle Horst witnessed a truck entering the area of the factory and breathed a sigh of relief. Frederic spoke to Horst what had happened. He related to Horst about the next transaction, which was to take place within two weeks. "You did well," Horst said. "Now go home, in peace. It is late."

Peter and Frederic drove home where Mary was becoming impatient. In the absence of Peter, Mary was very upset. She was considering about the season when he worked with Klaus. Mary's thought was, "What happened to them?" In the past, she gave the account to Peter about Klaus and Gertrude. Mary soon realized for security that they could not be contacted. The family believed that they would later reunite meeting again one day in a far better set of circumstances.

Two weeks passed. The time had finally come to retrieve the next pallet of materials. Mary arose very anxiously in the morning, and said to Peter, "I had a very bad dream. Do not go there. The dream was a premonition; they attacked you."

"What's next?" asked Frederic

"I do not know. I woke up," said Mary.

"The circumstance will be well just as before. We'll get it in one day," said Peter. Mary often had prophetic visions.

"Be alert and cautious," said Mary.

This occasion they took ample funds to load the truck with the pallets of materials. Frederic and Peter boarded the truck and drove quickly and as directly as possible to the border with Lithuania. They had no problem crossing the border; after an hour and a half, the men were at Lukas's factory. They greeted each other and immediately started talking about the business. "I'm sorry to tell you, that I have bad news for you," said the factory owner. "I have a portion of the material agreed upon. Most of the material is in the next town. My truck broke down and I didn't have time to find other drivers I could trust. Peter, you will have to go there and pick up the remaining material for your uncle."

Frederick looked at Peter and considered the difficult situation. "Why did you deceive us? You could simply ask someone to bring this cargo directly to you? After all, it is in your best interest," said Peter.

"My close friend has a truck. He was busy. I did not want to discuss critical issues. You know the times and season, currently," answered Lukas. "You must return within three hours," insisted the Lithuanian. Peter and Frederic came out of the office into the hallway and spoke directly.

Peter remembered the warning that Mary had said, "I do not like it. It is based on deceit."

Frederic looked at Peter and said, "Uncle Horst said that in all probability it is the last course. We cannot return without inventory. We have all the necessary papers on the trade; we are agreed then, to press on regardless of the cost."

"Frederic. This is our life," said Peter.

"One more," said Frederic.

"Okay. We're going. But we must keep our eyes wide open," said Peter. They returned to the office and informed the Lithuanian of their decision.

"I'll give you a man who will go with you and show you the way which is difficult to travel, less obvious. He will show you the path. This is my trusted man," said the Lithuanian. Frederic paid Lukas for his goods and went outside.

Frederic and Peter were accompanied by the Lithuanian. They rode away in a hurry. On the way, they passed a line of military trucks. There was a Lithuanian army regrouping large numbers of troops. An hour later the men were in town. This city was unknown to Peter and Frederic. They came to the warehouse but the entrance gate was closed. "What's going on here?" asked Peter.

"Wait here! I will come back," said the Lithuanian. He stepped out of the cab and walked along the fence of a large undisclosed building reminiscent of a warehouse. The Lithuanian disappeared in an opening in the fence.

Frederic and Peter saw him as he entered the small door of the building. "I do not like this. Let's be deliberately observant to keep an eye on the investment that you have made. It's a great deal of money," said Peter to Frederic.

In a matter of minutes, three men came out of the building; the Lithuanian and the two strangers. They went to the gate and one of them put the key into the lock and cautiously opened it. Then he pulled down a heavy chain and opened the metal of a rusted gate. When entering the warehouse, Peter looked at the two strangers; it was obvious that they were under the extreme pressure and influence of alcohol. The strangers pulled the heavy gate behind them closing it. Peter and Frederic did not know where to go. One of the men went to them encouraging them to drive to the back entrance of the building. "The foremen will open the door for you from the inside. The owner will be there waiting for you," said one of the strangers.

Frederic drove to the back of a long building. Peter with Frederic looked around inside anxiously searching. Finally, the door opened and the foremen ordered them to enter inside. Frequently, Peter and Frederic did this in other situations. This time, Frederic and Peter got out of the truck and stated that they desired to first talk to the owner. "No problem," replied the Lithuanian who smelled of alcohol. He waved at them and said, "Follow me," and began to walk towards something that could only be described as an office. Along the way, Peter and Frederic looked around the demolished building. Fortunately now open for deeper inspection. There was everything before them that was needed to build a house. In the adjoining room, Frederic noticed a complete inventory of a host of different materials. In the distance, they saw a light shining in the back administration room. They made their way through the maze of material with some effort. There, they went to the office.

The door opened to a broad-shouldered man. A small, fat, unshaven, unkempt man was sitting by the desk. The sight of Frederic and Peter caused him to stand up. He began to comment in Lithuanian, "I welcome you, my friends. I received a coded message that you were coming. All is prepared and ready. Do you have the money?" He then gave them a handshake.

"Yes we have the funds," said Frederic.

"Come now, I'll show you your inventory with the merchandise you require." Peter whispered to Frederic, "The underground forwarded the message. You can't trust the phone. It is tapped. All is in amiss here." The men entered through the corridor and went into a small room.

Peter and Frederic were attacked by four unknown men. Peter felt the blows and punches on his body. He began to defend himself. Frederic did the same. "Finish them," screamed the insane Lithuanian to his assembled thugs. Peter felt something sharp and stinging in his body. There was a powerful blow struck to his head, then a second and a third and final, powerful blow. Peter then lost consciousness. He collapsed on the floor next to Frederick, who was grasping his stomach. There was only silence. "Search them!" said the fat, putrid, vulgar Lithuanian to his subordinates. They searched and emptied their victim's pockets. They found on Peter and Frederic a large sum of money that was taken by the Lithuanian. Seeing the money the Lithuanian smiled and put everything into his pocket. Then he said, "Bring them to the forest, in the evening we will bury them! Hide the truck and remain outside the city. We'll meet here, tomorrow." He gave to each of them a sum of money and left the room.

Horst sat in his office waiting impatiently for the return of Frederic and Peter. "They should have been here, already. What delayed them? Perhaps they have already returned, unharmed," Horst said to himself. It was already ten in the evening and the men had not arrived home. Horst could not sit still in one place. Horst continued to walk around the factory waiting for Frederic and Peter to arrive.

Mary began to get anxiously impatient and upset. When evening came she began to pray. She believed that something had happened. Mary had no peace since Peter and Frederic left the house. She had not slept all night. Sitting on her rocking chair was all she could do.

In the morning she immediately looked out the window multiple times to see if someone would come with some important news. Mary could not go to the factory. Her sons John and Vladek were still fast asleep. It was 9 am. In came an employee. The employee was sent from Horst. "Peter and Frederic had not yet returned. Maybe the truck broke down. We are looking forward to their return," said an employee who walked back into the factory. Mary was now; completely, alone. She sat stiffly on a chair in the kitchen and again burst into tears.

Horst arrived late in the evening. He walked into the house and embraced Mary. He tried to encourage her. "I have no idea what happened to them. I will wait one more day and then send someone to Lithuania to check where they are. They had to be stopped. I can't encourage, you at this time," said Horst.

Mary sat down on the chair and embraced the children. They asked their mother where their Father was. "He'll return home soon," said Mary consoling them. Horst was discouraged for the moment, speaking to Mary and the children. He then he got up and then drove to the factory.

Horst was in the city office, speaking on this matter. Citizens told him of what the situation had become outside of Germany. There was very little that anyone could do within the current circumstances. The family asked him to go to Lithuania and intervene, immediately. Horst knew he could not drive himself there. He would be immediately recognized. Others were terrified, to go to Lithuania. Even if he sent someone unrecognized to Lithuania there was no guarantee that this person would go and report to the police. Horst was trapped. Two days passed. Horst found a man he felt he could trust; who had traveled to Lithuania and he knew that area well. Horst had no other choice he offered him money if he brought him the good news about Peter and Frederic. This select person, as an advocate, agreed and went directly to Lithuania.

Two additional days passed. A man sent by Horst to Lithuania reported to him with the sad news. "No one knows anything. The factory owner, Lukas, related the same story. They were there. They bought three pallets of material from him and left."

Horst wondered "Where did Peter and Frederic go?" No one really knew what happened except Lukas, who was lying.

"I was speaking with the local authorities and reported them missing. They have experienced turmoil throughout the town. The local area was overwhelmed with troops. The others won't overlook such matters. I'm sorry, but that's all I can do at this time," said the man hired by Horst.

"Thank you for your help. You have given the family hope. I will remember this," said Horst and he handed the man the commission they agreed to. They departed in silence and ended the conversation.

Horst sat on his chair in the office and began to ponder. He could not accept the loss of Frederic. He was the last and closest friend to his family. Peter was missing. Horst was tormented. He had sent Peter and Frederic to Lithuania to earn more income. It was a risk not worth doing. "What would Mary do with the children without Peter?" Horst asked himself. Horst believed that he must demonstrate responsibility and care for them.

The following day, Horst went to Mary, she was discouraged and inconsolable. She made a cup of coffee and they both sat down at the table pondering the previous night's conversation. Mary saddened asked Horst, "What am I to do now? I have no home to return to. The house was taken over by the Germans. I cannot go back to Gertrude. I will be alone with the children."

"Listen Mary," said Horst. "I'm old. I have a big house. Move in with me with the children John and Vladek. We will be more comfortable in these difficult times. We'll wait this out."

Chapter IX
Memory loss

A N ELDERLY WOMAN WENT FOR a slow walk; bowed by the burden of a bundle of branches on her back. The winter fast approached. The old woman went dutifully to the forest every day to gather as much wood as possible for the winter. She was close to her home. "Which way should I go?" thought the old woman. "Today, I will take another path near the gorge." She passed by the most dangerous place near the cliff. It was then she saw that something was lying on the bottom of the ravine. She paused for a moment and then tried to stare with her eyes at the object. Her vision was failing due to old age. She could not recognize what it was. "Those vaporous eyes now see only shadows. Old age brings complete blindness," the old woman said to herself. She began to walk away.

The old woman was thinking all the way home. This thought did not give her peace. "What was there in the gorge?" she thought to herself. "I must go and see what lies in the ravine." Aldona dropped the branches within the shed. The woman saw her husband and said, "Stephen I have to tell you something."

"You are complaining again? Can't you realize that I'm busy," said the old man.

"What are you doing?" asked the woman.

"I am thinking while I smoke a pipe," said Stephen.

"What I have to say is more important," insisted the old women. "Listen to me, Stephen. I was walking through the forest with a bundle of branches near a ravine. In the distance, I saw a body lying at the bottom of the ravine. I did not recognize what it was because I had weak, failing eyes."

"That is not my problem," said Stephen sharply with ridicule.

"But yesterday I went on that familiar path and no one was there. Someone fell into the gorge and maybe needs help. Stephan, can you come with me and see what happened there? We will see then what lies there," the old crone insisted.

Stephen stood up and looked at his wife and said, "Aldona, why do you want to involve yourself? Why do I always listen to you?"

The couple both walked slowly towards the forest. Aldona asked, "Stephan. Why do I have to continually argue with you?" Stephan did not answer and went ahead.

Stephen was impatient and in a hurry. It required a long time to arrive at the place described by the crone, Aldona. They were now walking in a narrow gorge. Surveying, near the high embankment between the bushes, Stephen saw something, "unidentified." He came closer and saw two human bodies drenched in blood. "God, what is this? Bodies…" Stephen said loudly. Aldona covered her mouth with despair when she saw the bloody corpse. Stephen stepped closer. There were marks on the bodies from inhumane stabbing by a knife. He threw this first body on his back. It was cold. "He's stiff, long dead," Stephen told Aldona. "War creates this reality. We must look the other way."

He went to a second body which lay nearby. He grabbed the cold limp body by the hand. It was moving. He put his ear to his chest and said, "That one is still breathing. We have to make an effort to save him."

"What will we do?" asked Aldona.

"I know what we will do. I have a plan. Let's go home," said Stephan. This time, Stephen was walking at a faster pace. Aldona could not keep up with him.

When they returned to the home, Stephen said to his wife, "You boil water and prepare bandages. Do not speak to anyone about this. I am taking a horse from the barn with a winter sledge. The entrance to the ravine is narrow; a wagon will not fit there, only a sleigh. I'll be back." He prepared a horse and a sleigh. This time of the year, there was no snow. The horse was pulling the sleigh on the grass. When he arrived at the ravine where the bodies were slain, he put the wounded man on the sledge and tied him with a rope so that he would not fall off the sledge. He looked at the other body and said to himself, "I will bury him tomorrow."

Stephen's house was at the edge of the clearing before the boundary of the forest. He drove up to the door and with his wife Aldona they brought the wounded man inside their home. They laid him on a bed carefully prepared by Aldona in a small room at the back of the house. Aldona immediately began to wash the body of the wounded man. Her shaking hands held scissors. She cut off the bloody shirt and pants and checked wounds. There were many bruises on the body. She sewed three stab wounds. "It's probably from the knife and the brutal beating," Stephen said.

"His jaw is broken and ribs are bruised. Surely, he has a lot of internal injuries. They beat him well," said Aldona. They both cleaned the wounds and put more bandages over the man. Later, they prayed for the survival and recovery of this unknown man. They were showing the man some dignity and mercy.

The following day Stephen took a long piece of fabric and a shovel and went to the gorge to bury the body of the second man. The soil was rocky and hard. He had just seen the grotesque corpses that were wounded. The head was smashed from the impact of something heavy. He had two stab wounds and a broken leg. Stefan surveyed the scene and came to the conclusion that someone had dropped them from the cliff into the ravine as discarded refuse. He grabbed the shovel and started digging down. It took him almost two hours to dig a deep hole three feet down. Finally, he dragged the body of the stranger to the grave and covered him with the fabric. He stood over the grave, took off his hat and said a very short prayer. "I am sorry, I don't know your name," then he covered the corpse with earth. Tired, he slowly returned home.

When Stephen returned home, Aldona was sitting in the kitchen and asked, "Did you bury him?"

"Oh yes. He was terribly wounded," said Stefan. "Someone had beaten them well." Aldona pondered "What happened?" Only they knew. How long did the beating take? "When he recovers he will tell us everything?" said Aldona. Every day Aldona was staring at the stranger. Three days passed and the wounded man was still unconscious. He continued to sleep.

The wounds were healing well. On the fourth day, the stranger began to moan and move his broken fingers. Stefan and Aldona were pleased to see that the signs of life were returning. "He has the will to live," said Stefan.

The stranger began to rave more and more. He opened his eyes and looked at the ceiling. Relatives, other Spirits of the dead were calling to him. Aldona at that time gave him a home remedy to drink. Aldona and Stephen watched him alternately. On the fifth day, the stranger opened his eyes and began to look around. He saw Stephen sitting in a chair and quietly asked in one language and then correcting himself in Polish, "Where am I?"

Stephen knew a little Polish and said, "You are in Lithuania. We found you in a gorge. You were beaten and severely wounded by others. You've been lying here for a little more than a week." The stranger closed his eyes and was silent. He opened his eyes again and struggled to move and then to breath, but a terrible pain pierced his body. He grimaced and convulsed. He lay back on the bed. Stephen gave the wounded man tea, and medicine to drink and said, "You are doing well. Go to sleep. Sleep is health." After a few minutes; the stranger fell asleep.

The wounds on his head and body began to heal. The dizziness began to subside. Finally, came the day when the stranger sat on the bed and asked, "How did this happen that I am here?" Stefan, sitting with Aldona on the edge of the bed, told him the account of how he came to be there. "I do not remember details or events of where I was," said the stranger.

In this occasion they both spoke in Lithuanian. "How did you come to know our language?"

The stranger thought for a moment and said, "My mind is not clear."

"What is your name?" Stefan continued.

The stranger began to think, and after a minute he simply answered. "I do not know. I cannot remember. Give me a name. Later, when my name comes to me, I'll tell you. I have a lot of pain, in my head."

Aldona gave the stranger tea as a special remedy to sleep so that he could lie calmly and peacefully. His head and body will heal quickly. Finally, the day came when the stranger sat on the bed and asked, "How did it happen that I am here?" Stephen sitting with Aldona on a chair he pulled up beside the bed and told him, again what happened. "I do not remember anything," said the stranger.

This time they both conversed in Lithuanian. "How do you know our language?"

The stranger thought for a moment, and simply said, "I do not know.

"What is your name, and where do you originate?" continued Stephen.

The stranger began to think and after a moment he answered "I do not know. I cannot recall."

"Someone has beaten you very well," said Aldona. After a while, Aldona gave him the medicine and the stranger went to bed.

"We'll talk again tomorrow," said Stephen.

In the morning the stranger awoke in his bed. He slowly lowered his legs from the bed and painfully tried to stand. He was in a weakened condition. Stefan and Aldona held him on both sides so that he did not fall over. "Everything hurts me. Mostly my ribs," said the stranger as he put his hand to his ribs on the right side. He took a few steps and fell down on the bed again.

"You have to rest for a moment. Someone fixed you really good," said Aldona.

"I do not understand. Why did you say, you?" asked the stranger.

"In the gorge where we found you, you were with another one, a man who was dead. I buried him. We brought you here. Do you remember who he was? What happened? Who beat you?" asked Stephen.

The stranger thought a moment and replied, "I really do not remember. I do not know what happened," he gripped his head.

"Come into the kitchen, and eat breakfast. Come to the table with us," said Aldona and together with Stephen helped the man to the kitchen; during breakfast, Stephen informed the stranger of what was happening.

Two more weeks passed, and Mary had as yet, no news about Peter. Horst did all he could to find out about what happened to Frederic and Peter. Everyone was silent. "Maybe someone knew something but was afraid to talk," thought Horst. Horst offered money to provide any current information. But, no one came forward. The factory was run by Horst's friend. Horst was not fit for any specific job. The situation with the disappearance of Frederic and Peter developed a deep spirit of depression in Horst. Melancholia had taken away his desire to live. After three weeks, Mary was forced to move to Horst's house. They lived on the second floor, while Horst resided on the first floor. Vladek continued asking about his father. Mary replied that he left for work to a faraway place and that he would be back soon. She still knew that one day he would see him step through the door.

Stephen and Aldona diligently cared for the wounded man so that he would recover as soon as possible. They treated him like their own son. Aldona and Stephen's son died when he was seven years old. The wounded man did not remember the details of his life or his common name. They named him Matas. Matas was getting stronger. He stayed quietly at home. None of the neighbors knew that Aldona and Stephen were hiding someone in their home. Matas sat motionless for hours and thought. Occasionally, he began to speak in Polish, again in German, and with Stephen and Aldona talking in Lithuanian. How he knew these languages, he did not know.

A month passed as Matas was living with Stephen and Aldona. Matas felt stronger every day. There was now only one problem; Matas could not remember his past. It all began when he was severely beaten. Stephen and Aldona were afraid to go to the police, and tell everything; how they found Matas and the other man. They said, if someone tried to kill them, they would surely try to do it again. In the time of war, everything was possible. Who knows who did it? Stephen and Aldona were afraid for their lives.

Chapter X
Captivity

AT THE END OF JUNE 1940, Russia entered Lithuania. Uprising against Russia broke out. The population was against the occupation of its territories by Russia. Stalin, the leader of Russia, at the expense of millions of human lives, wanted to enlarge the Russian occupation. He wished to make Russia a powerful force in the world. Russia was the conqueror of the Baltic Nations for its own needs and propaganda.

Life in the village was peaceful until the arrival of Russian soldiers. They went forth from house to house and harassed everyone. Whenever they confiscate a pig or a cow, they would say it's for the need of the army. A Russian officer entered the house of Stephen and Aldona. The Russian checked all the rooms, pulled out a notebook and asked, "How many live here?"

"My wife and I," replied Stephen.

The Russian looked at Stephen and asked, "Whose things are in the little room?"

Stephen replied, "These are my nephew's belongings. But, he is not with us, today. He was only here temporarily." The soldier looked suspiciously at Stephen and Aldona and recorded his survey in his notebook. He procured a loaf of bread from the table and left. Stefan and Aldona breathed a sigh of relief. Stephen was tipped off that the Russians were in the village. Earlier in the morning he ordered Matas immediately to flee, within the forest, and wait there, until evening. They would then bring him word when the danger had passed.

October 1940; The Russians unexpectedly arrived with two trucks at the village where Stephen, Aldona, and Matas lived. Matas at this time had no way of escaping into the forest. The village was surrounded. The Russians rounded up all of the young, healthy men who were now eligible to join the army. Among them was Matas. Stephen and Aldona wept after losing Matas. To the end, they did not know who he was but never lost hope that they would one day be reunited.

Mary supervised the children. Horst treated her like his own daughter. John and Vladek grew up and continued asking the same questions, about their father. Mary was constantly telling them that her father was far away at work and would soon return. The factory was working in full swing, shifts of 14 hours a day. Slowly everyone forgot painful memories of the missing men. Mary diligently prayed in the evening. She was a woman of deep faith, conviction, and perseverance. At the border, there was the escalation of more and more troops. The common people said that the Germans would ultimately invade Russia.

The Russians transported all the inducted young men from the villages to a specially prepared camp. Most of the officers were Russian and some Lithuanian. When Matas stood in front of the identity officer, he asked, "Name and surname?"

"Matas Zukas."

"Date of birth and town of residence?"

Here Matas randomly chose a date of birth and said, "September 16, 1912." He gave the place of his birth as the name of the village, where he lived with Stefan and Aldona. Officially Matas was in the army. The training was intense to help them be prepared to be mentally and physically conditioned to be soldiers and handle the stresses of war.

The bitter winter arrived. The soldiers lived in barracks heated by coal. Many times the assigned soldier of the watch, who was responsible for guarding the stove at night, fell asleep. Everyone woke up with morning frostbite. The winter was hard and cold. Matas's supervisors noted his diligence. Matas was very bright and had the ability to speak Polish and German. He was posted to the platoon educating the officers. Apart from the daily ritual of exercises that took place outside in the cold. Matas learned of military activities and gossip within the camp.

Spring of 1941. Matas was sent together with his assigned unit near the border with Germany a hundred miles from the village of Stephen and Aldony. The Russians armed themselves and prepared for an extended conflict and did not believe the grandiose announcements about peace. The Germans were not to be bluffed and armed themselves for power. The line of the German-Russian border from the north to the south, which ran along the Narew, Bug and San rivers, was encircled by the strength of the German army. Mildew hung in the air. It smelled of war; more devastation and corpses.

On June 22, 1941, Hitler launched his armies eastward in a massive invasion of the Soviet Union: three great army groups with over three million German soldiers, 150 divisions with fortifications of three thousand tanks smashed across the frontier into Soviet territory. The invasion covered a front from the North Cape to the Black Sea, a distance of two thousand miles. German combat offensives had reached its apogee; in training, doctrine, and fighting ability, foot soldiers invading Russia represented the finest army the world had ever seen in the modern era. Barbarossa was the crucial turning point in World War II.

The Nazis of Germany fought a two-front war against a coalition, possessing immensely superior resources. The Germans, however, had overlooked serious deficiencies. In hast, they severely underestimated their opponents; their logistical preparations were grossly inadequate for long-term campaigns. German industrial preparations for a sustained war had yet to begin. The greatest mistake that the Germans made was to come as conquerors, not as vilified liberators. The Germans were determined to enslave the Slavic population and exterminate the Jews. Thus, from the beginning, the war in the East became an inconclusive ideological struggle, waged with a ruthlessness and despotic mercilessness enemy not seen in Europe since the Mongols.

In Barbarossa's opening month, German Vehrmacht bit deep into the Soviet territory! The force and influx of troops and panzer armies encircled large Soviet forces at Minsk and Smolensk, while armored spearheads reached two-thirds of the distance to Moscow and Leningrad. German logistics of command were fatigued and unraveling. A series of Soviet counterattacks stalled the advance. In September, the Germans quickly moved supplies forward to renew their drives; the results were the encirclement battles of Kiev, in September, and Bryansk-Vyazma in October, each netting 600,000 prisoners.

Moscow lay open to the German advance. Russian weather intervened with heavy rains that turned the roads into trenches of mud and ice. The frosts of November solidified the mud. The drive could not resume. Despite the lateness of the season and the fact that further advances would leave their troops with no shelter; winter clothes or supply dumps for the winter. The generals urged Hitler to continue. The German troops struggled to dominate the stronghold gates of Moscow where Soviet counterattacks stopped them in early December. The desperate conditions continued and they conducted a slow retreat as more Soviet attacks threatened to envelop much of their forces. Details which befell Napoleon's Grand Army in 1812. In the end, the Soviets overextended their defensive, and the Germans restored order to the front line. The spring thaw in March 1942 brought operations to a halt. Barbarossa had failed; Nazi Germany confronted a two-front war that it could not prevail.

The unit, in which Matas served, was poorly armed. The Germans began to smash through the border. The offensive used tanks and planes. The primitive Russian aviation was immediately destroyed. The section defended by Matas' platoon was attacked by a German division using machine guns, armored cars, and tanks. The Russian and Lithuanian troops defending this region had limited heavy equipment and far fewer soldiers than the well-fortified Germans. The fight was short with heavy losses. The Russians suffered extreme casualties in soldiers and equipment. Matas withdrew together with many others. Matas' platoon suffered heavy losses with only a few soldiers left. Fleeing from the Germans, Matas heard a powerful explosion in the rear. The force of the concussion impact lifted him into the air, throwing him violently to the hard earth. Matas lost consciousness.

Chapter XI
Meeting with Klaus

MATAS WITH A HOST OF Lithuanian soldiers were captured. He woke up lying on the open ground next to many wounded casualties. Matas' uniform was torn, dirty and blood-soaked; he had a bandage wrapped around his head. Matas had a pounding headache and a constant ringing in his ears. The Germans surrounded the perimeter where they were being held within the encampment of barbed wire. After three days, Matas, together with other wounded prisoners walked parallel with a column of soldiers about 7 miles before they reached the train station where they were loaded in captured railway wagons. The Germans abducted only those prisoners who could walk. The rest of them were unnecessary, expendable and eliminated. The prisoner's train departed and after about three hours stopped at the Gusen.

The prisoners later exited out of the archaic wagons. They found themselves in Stalag 18 designed for prisoners of war. A high barbed wire fence surrounded the camp. The Stalag was fully secured and guarded by high towers. Prisoners were then put into wooden barracks. Matas was assigned a lower bunk at the end of the barracks. There were two additional bunks above him. At night you could hear the moans and yells of the wounded. Every day prisoners gathered in the open square. Those who fell and could not stand at attention on their feet were quickly marked, secured, and taken away by the Germans to be disposed of.

Days and weeks passed. Matas was steadily and consistently recovering. For many nights Matas had strange flashes with shadows of memory. He often heard the voice of a woman slowly whispering and calling out to him, "Peter, Peter." Week to week he recalled more and more of the former details of a life that was now, a distant mystery to him.

Stalag 18 held approximately three thousand prisoners. The prisoners worked in seven large barracks supplying the needs of the German army. The first initial month, passed. Matas was assigned to work in one of the barracks. Finishing the daily assigned work; Matas with the prisoners, walked to his barracks. His path was crossed by two Germans who passed by the prisoners. One German was in uniform, the other in civilian clothes. The civilian stopped and inspected a group of prisoners. He was looking inside for Matas. The other man, dressed in civilian clothes said to his friend, "You go and I'll be right there." The civilian began to follow a group of prisoners. He carefully watched for the door where Matas entered. He then turned and walked, toward the building where the camp commander was stationed.

The next day, the civilian entered the building where Matas worked and watched him very closely. The unknown man entered the small commander's office and asked about one specific prisoner. "A good and diligent worker; productive," replied the German responsible for the operations in his barracks.

"Call him," said the civilian. Prisoners in the camp knew this particular civilian. He was the right hand of the camp commander responsible for work operations and daily construction of the camp. After a while, perhaps 5 minutes, Matas was in the office. "What is your name?" asked the German in a prompt civil tone.

"Matas Zukas," answered Matas in German not knowing why he spoke in that dialect.

"Oh, you speak German, very well," said the German as he looked straight into Matas' eyes.

The personal scrutiny lasted for a while and finally, the German said, "From tomorrow on, he will work for me; bring him to me promptly at eight o'clock." He then ordered the guards to escort Matas to the daily work site.

Matas tried to understand the greatest reason for the secret conversations with the German. Looking sharply in the Germans eyes, Matas felt as though he knew him. Though he could not remember where he knew him. His memory continued to fail him. His past life was a dark fog hidden behind a veil of mist.

The following day, Matas went to work with the German. The Germans as a precaution did everything to make sure no one was around (to witness their conversations). "Sit down," said the German. "Where are you from?"

"I am from Lithuania," said Matas, who was surprised. He did not know why the German allowed him to sit down.

"What languages do you speak?" asked the German.

"I can speak Polish, Russian, Lithuanian and German. Is that sufficient?" replied Matas. "Do we know each other, from somewhere? Have we been introduced?"

The German spoke up and said, "Olsztyn, Klaus, Gertrude." Matas listened to these names and tried to remember something, anything. Though familiar, he knew the names but could not associate from where. "John, Vladek, Mary." At the word, "Mary," Matas shook.

He knew the pronounced sound of the dialect but, he did not know from what region. "Please forgive me, I have memory problems."

Then the German approached Matas, grabbed him by the shoulders and said, "I am Klaus, your cousin." He observed Matas' reaction and continued, "You have a scar about, two inches above your right breast."

Matas unbuttoned his shirt and saw the scar. "How did he know that?" he asked himself? Matas looked again and squinted at the German.

"Do not be afraid. I have already told you, I'm your cousin from Olsztyn. Your name is Peter Mayer. You have a wife Mary, and two sons John and Vladek," said Klaus.

Matas listened to this as if he were enchanted. Something reminded him of those names, but he did not know where he first heard them. Klaus said, "Do not say anything to anyone of what you heard here. Today, I am busy, but tomorrow, we will talk again. Go to the back and tend to your cleaning. No one will bother you, here." Klaus tightly embraced Peter and then said,

"Glad to see you. I thought we would never see each other again. Everything will be fine. Do what I told you," and he walked out of the room.

Peter stood still, motionless for a moment and thought about what he had heard from the mouth of the German, who revealed to him that he was his cousin. How did he know of his forgotten past of which, he had no idea? The name of Mary was in his memory. Matas thought of this to himself, "I have two children John and Vladek." He could not believe it. "Maybe it's all true," thought Peter, while cleaning. The entire day he continued to struggle with these tormenting thoughts.

Klaus realized that Peter, who is named Matas, had problems with memory. He supervised Peter, under his care. With the permission of the camp commander, Peter was then, only available, to Klaus' personal disposition. Klaus was a "special" civilian in the Stalag 18 camp. Everyone respected him. He was here from the beginning, when the camp was constructed. Klaus built the camp with his own hands. He was proud of the work. Klaus, with disappointment, knew that his work would be used to keep prisoners in confinement. He was very melancholy, about this. He could not tolerate seeing how the Nazis tormented the prisoners. Too many prisoners lost their sanity and their lives.

The days and weeks passed. Daily conversation with Klaus yielded to Peter more details about the past. It was indeed, a turbulent time for both of them. Over time, Peter was gaining a trust and confidence in Klaus. After three months, Peter knew very well, who he was, and where he lived. Peter's real name was changed to Wise. Peter knew that when he escaped from Olsztyn, Klaus's friend, Ted, helped him. Deep in conjecture, his memory again clouded. Peter then tried to remember some important details of life before finding himself in Stephen's and Aldona home. Two details were lodged in his head. The first detail was that, he remembered, he was employed in a factory, where they sewed clothes and in the second detail, he was attacked and wounded by someone, he didn't recognize. Stephen told him that he was with another man; who, according to Stephen's testimony, was killed. Who was that man? Why was he killed? What did they do in Lithuania? Peter had no idea.

Klaus was arrested and sent into exile to Gusen, to the Stalag 18 camp. He had no contact with Gertrude. He gained the favor of the camp commander by effectively building the barracks quickly and within budget. Klaus was then allowed to see his wife, Gertrude. Occasionally, she visited him in the camp. Klaus and Gertrude agreed that she would be living in Olsztyn.

Gertrude came to visit Klaus; it was two months after Klaus recognized Peter. Quietly, Klaus said to Gertrude that Peter was confined in the Camp. Gertrude was surprised by this news and cried with delight. Klaus explained Peter's situation, he was alive. He then ordered Gertrude to find the old coachman, Ted. Maybe Ted would know where Peter went with his family. Gertrude then vowed to keep everything a secret and not to divulge a single word.

Klaus spent many hours of time with Peter, who was more aware of his past. Peter's problem with his memory, continued to make him feel melancholy. He could not remember where Mary was with the children. He did not remember or know what they looked like. Klaus described the appearance of Mary, John, and Vladek but this was not enough for Peter. There was no association in his mind with their appearances or their ages. Where had they gone? Were they adults or children?

A month passed, Gertrude came to visit Klaus. She found Old Ted in good spirits. Ted was very pleased to see Gertrude. They talked for a long time. When Gertrude asked about Peter and his family Ted told her where he had taken Peter, with the select location where he intended to hide. Ted mentioned a town, Stalapen, in the immediate vicinity close to the border of Germany and Lithuania, where his friend Frederic lived. Ted stated that Frederic worked in a factory that sewed clothing and various sundry items. Gertrude asked Ted to meet her one day for tea. He said he would be happy to.

Klaus was very pleased with this news. Unfortunately, he did not know how to locate Mary with the children. Germany controlled everything. The resistance movement against the Nazis intensified throughout occupied Poland and former Prussia. The Germans were exceedingly ruthless toward the people and the original places where the resistance came from. They burned, robbed and killed the people who resisted them.

Klaus ultimately realized that the only person who could locate the factory was Gertrude. The final decision belonged to her. Gertrude had a special pass issued by the commander of Stalag 18 for free movement around former East Prussia which was now the territory of Germany. Before she departed, Klaus asked her if she could find Frederic. Gertrude was anxious. She understood what a difficult and dangerous task this was. One conversation or question with a misidentified person brought the threat of imprisonment and perhaps death. "I'll think about it," she replied.

Gertrude was surprised to see that Peter was alive; on the other hand, she was saddened by Mary and her children's unusual situation. She did not know what to do. The Germans did not have mercy on those who acted against them and on the other hand, she wanted to find Mary. After two weeks, Gertrude said to herself, "If I find someone who has a family or friends in Stalapen, I'll go there and try again to find Mary. But how do I know she's still there? Maybe she has left town?" Many questions and uncertainties remained in Gertrude's mind.

Gertrude cautiously began to question her friends about Stalapen, mentioned by Ted. Finally, after a week, Gertrude was at her friend's house. She was met there by her second cousin Brigit, who said she had a distant cousin elsewhere. She was there a number of times before the war. Brigit said there was a municipal factory sewing various clothes. Gertrude's heart began to beat harder, and then she broke down.

"What has happened to you?" asked the woman sitting with Gertrude

"Nothing, serious it's just a slight weakness. From time to time I have my anxious moments," answered Gertrude. After the shocking news, Gertrude said goodbye to her friends and went home.

After an additional two days, Gertrude visited Ingrid. During the conversation, she learned that Ingrid and her cousin Brigit did not like the Germans. Gertrude began to inquire asking her about her cousin Brigit. Ingrid then realized what was going on. Ingrid cautioned Gertrude and said that she could trust Brigit. Ingrid said, "I do not know what you're going to do; I recommend that you come here in approximately three days, at two, in the afternoon. I'll make an effort to get her here to talk to you."

Gertrude then courteously thanked Ingrid and went home. "Now there was no turning back," Gertrude thought to herself. When the Germans abducted Klaus in 1939 Gertrude sold the business and all machinery, two trucks and a car to a German friend. Until now, Gertrude lived very modestly on the stipend of money and savings that Klaus invested in a bank.

Three days passed and Gertrude visited Ingrid's house, where her cousin was already residing. Gertrude then put everything on the table and explained to Ingrid's cousin Brigit the whole situation. That she had to go to Stalapen, where Ingrid's cousin lived and to locate someone in the city. "Can I count on your help... with the help of your cousin?" asked Gertrude.

"Yes. You can count on Thomas. He detests the Germans," said Brigit. "When you want to go there, I'll give you a letter of introduction addressed to him. I know he will help you."

"I want to go there next week," said Gertrude. Brigit said that she would gladly prepare a letter to her cousin, Thomas and bring it to Ingrid in a few days. The women talked privately for a moment and then returned to their homes.

Seven days later Gertrude rode on the train. It was by then a snowy and freezing winter. The train stopped in Stalapen, where Brigit's cousin lived. Gertrude exited the train and went on foot to the indicated address by Brigit. After fifteen minutes she was standing in front of Thomas's house. Gertrude pressed the bell. Her heart was beating rapidly, from excitement. "What will happen if he doesn't want to help me? What will I do then?" Gertrude asked herself.

Time passed and the door opened. A tall man stood in the doorway. "I am Gertrude. I want to speak to Thomas," said Gertrude.

"That would be me," replied the man.

"I have a letter from Brigit," and she gave the letter to Thomas. Thomas then stepped forward, leaned out looked left and then right and invited Gertrude inside.

"Please go into the living room," and he gestured to where she had to go.

The kitchen revealed a neatly dressed woman. Thomas introduced his wife, whose name was Helen. Thomas said, "This lady is sent from Brigit. Everyone, please sit down." When everyone sat down, Thomas began to read the letter. When he finished reading the letter he said, "Now, we can talk. I have full confidence in Brigit. Please take off your coat and we will discuss this matter." Gertrude breathed a sigh of relief. Thomas asked his wife to bring hot tea and coffee for everyone.

After a while, they were sitting at the table and Thomas asked, "How can I help you?" Gertrude explained to them the primary reason why she came here. "Yes, there is a factory that sews dry goods and clothing. The owner's name is Horst," said Thomas.

"Is there also a helpful man named Frederic?" asked Gertrude.

"Yes, there was, but he disappeared a year ago in Lithuania with one of the workers from the factory. What was the name of the other young man?" Thomas asked Helen.

Helen thought about this for a moment, and said, "His name was Peter." Gertrude became very emotional and was excited. Thomas and Helen sat in complete silence until Gertrude calmed down. "I would like to meet with Horst. Can you arrange a meeting?" asked Gertrude.

"Today it's getting late. Tomorrow in the morning I will go directly to the factory. Tonight, you can rest with us," said Thomas. Thomas, Helen, and Gertrude were sitting speaking in a long exhausting conversation about the current situation of the war. Late in the evening, they went to sleep.

In the morning; while it was dark Thomas exited the house and went to the factory. There, he asked to speak to Horst; after five minutes, one of the employees led Thomas to the office of Horst. Horst sat at his desk and asked, "What events do you want to talk to me about?"

"Very private information," said Thomas with these words. Horst ordered his other employees in his office, to leave immediately. Horst and Thomas were now alone. It was their moment for both of them.

Thomas began "There is a woman in my house named Gertrude. She in all likelihood will want to talk to you."

Horst looked at Thomas and asked, "About what?"

Thomas looked at Horst and said, "She is asking about Frederic."

At that, Horst stiffened. "What did you say?" asked Horst, who was surprised.

Thomas repeated, "She asked about Frederic. She has some important news for you," said Thomas.

Horst abruptly stood up from his chair and said, "Can you lead her to me?"

"Of course, I can. You'll be relieved to know she's living at my home," said Thomas.

"We'll go there, now; with my car," said Horst and walked out of the office together with Thomas.

They drove directly to Thomas's home. As they entered the house, Helen and Gertrude sat in the kitchen drinking black coffee. After their official welcoming, Horst sat down by the table. Gertrude began to tell Horst the current events that she knew. Horst wept at the sad news of the violent, sudden death of Frederic. He was encouraged and relieved that Peter was alive. "I'll take you to Mary as soon as possible," said Horst.

"Is Mary here?" asked Gertrude.

"Yes. She and her children live with me," said Horst. Gertrude was happy with joy at the news, that she would finally meet Mary. Horst graciously thanked Thomas for his help. They entered into his car and drove away.

Mary ate breakfast with John and Vladek. She heard the car coming up the road; encouraged, she knew that it must be Horst's car. After a moment, the kitchen door opened and Gertrude and Horst entered. Mary seeing her burst into tears and threw herself into the arms of Gertrude. Both cried and with them wept Horst as well. John and Vladek were sitting at the table surprised, not really knowing what was going on. Mary called out to each of her children and said, "This is Aunt Gertrude, we stayed with her in Olsztyn."

Gertrude kissed John and Vladek and hugged them. "Mother, is father finally coming home?" asked Vladek.

Mary, not surprised said, "Not yet my dear son, but very soon."

"When?" asked Vladek again.

"I do not know yet," answered, Mary and embraced Vladek and John. Later that morning, everyone was celebrating at the table drinking hot tea and black coffee.

Mary asked Gertrude, "Tell me how you found us here?"

Gertrude looked at Mary and said, "Mary, Peter is most assuredly alive!" At these words, Mary's cup of tea fell from her hand and spilled across the table. Without looking at it, Mary put her hands to her mouth and she began to rejoice. Horst began to wipe up the spilled tea with a towel.

A moment later, Mary said, "I felt that he was alive. I prayed day by day, that God by providence would send him back to us. Where is he?" Here again, Gertrude told her the entire story. Mary was overjoyed, crying happy tears, embracing her children. "Father lives! My dear Peter is alive," Mary kissed John and Vladek. Both of them were young enough not to understand, what was accomplished, but were happy with their mother at the news that she shared with them.

The conversation ensued with great deliberation, they came to a reasonable arrangement that Horst and Gertrude would be visiting each other and sharing information about Klaus and Peter. Mary desired to see Peter but that was impossible. He was sanctioned, not available as a prisoner of war. Horst said that he would think on how to resolve the matter when he returned to his office; without telling anyone about the situation. It was a long eventful day. Mary and Gertrude talked late into the night. Finally, tired, they went to sleep after they finished their coffee.

Gertrude stayed with Mary for a week. It was now, time to go home. Gertrude was very reassured to find Mary with her children. They both said their goodbyes and Horst took Gertrude to the train. Gertrude stepped on the train, and returned to her home; she was thinking about current events that had happened. As she boarded the train, she again thought about how Klaus would react, especially Peter, with the good news, of what she was carrying.

This was great and shocking news especially for Peter, who then did not remember the resemblance, within his memory of Mary or his children. He relied only on what Klaus spoke into his mind, his heart pounding about his family. They both talked about this every day. Peter with great difficulty began to regain his memory, slowly remembering hazy details. The stress and disappointment confused him. Slowly vague glimpses came into his thoughts and he was hopeful and encouraged.

Several months passed. Germany captured new prisoners in great numbers; expanding to three million Russian soldiers. A difficult time and season had come. Stalag 18 was introduced with other prisoners from the eastern front, with a longstanding conflict between Germany and Russia. Neglect and poor treatment of prisoners caused starvation and deliberate deaths.

Klaus and Peter still lived in Stalag 18, which was significantly improved, thanks to the work of the prisoners. A great number of prisoners died from exhaustion, as a result of the work. Day after day new prisoners arrived. The Germans did not have mercy on a single one of them. Peter was no longer living in primitive barracks. Overcrowding was becoming a congestive problem. Klaus moved him to a building where there were better accommodations. There, Peter built a small room to be able to move in, immediately. Peter and Klaus were continually thinking about how to escape. They through necessity devised many unique and divergent plans. This hope gave them the desire to stay alive.

Horst's factory did not prosper in these turbulent times of war. He thought about closing the factory. He knew that the German banks were not insured or safe. All the money was deposited in Swiss accounts. His finances were safe and secure. Horst thought about escaping. Where to go wondered Horst? Horst had many connections. He had to leave the problem alone. But this was about Mary, John, Vladek and now, Peter. He felt guilty for the difficult situation he had placed himself in. He wanted to do what was best for everyone. Horst did not have the privilege of a close family. He finally decided to help Mary and Peter. He empowered them as future inheritors of his wealth and willed to each of them, his final inheritance and testament.

The Russians were on the offensive and conquered beleaguered national territories captured by the Germans. The situation became more and more intense and more desperate each day. The Germans, though aggressive, were already pushed back, to the borders of Lithuania and Belarus.

It was now September 1943. Horst decided to go immediately in haste to Gertrude. "I will return within two weeks. There is something I must do," said Horst to Mary. "Here, take the money for living expenses; watch the children," said Horst and put a large sum of money on the table and left. Horst liked John and Vladek. He loved and respected them like his own grandchildren.

Klaus and Peter continued to labor together. Klaus daily reminded Peter of his previous life. Peter slowly regained his memory. Gertrude returned from her trip with surprisingly, good news. A great measure of faith came to Peter in remembering his past. After the enthusiastic news, that Mary, John, and Vladek were healthy and waiting for him. Peter was an enthusiastic man with an ignited hope. He could not sleep all night. Peter and Klaus thought continually about a plot to escape. Hardships of life within the camp did not pass well for them.

The Germans knew very well that sooner or later, some prisoners would be relocated to secondary camps. Prisoners were suffering acutely in all camps by overcrowding and disease. Food rations were getting reduced to smaller and smaller rations. Many were dying daily of plague, hunger, hopelessness, and exhaustion. The numbers of prisoners were not arriving in the same numbers by this time. There were now 5,000 in the camp. Klaus understood that working in the camp broke his spirit down. Klaus and Peter again considered the possibilities on how to escape.

The Russians openly attacked the Germans on all fronts. The ultimate goal was to go to Berlin. The endless questions on everyone's mind became..., "Will Germany be occupied by Russia?" All over Europe, there was a monumental movement of resistance; and excitement against the Nazis. England and the United States were thinking of invasion. That would begin a land war with Germany in Europe. The expectant question of the hour was, "Who would arrive first to Berlin? The American army or the Russian army?"

Gertrude was at home when Horst came to her; she was surprised and relieved. Horst explained to Gertrude why he came. He then ordered her to contact Klaus and asked if he could arrange to escape from Stalag 18 together with Peter. Horst proceeded to say that he had an inside connection. He would handle new notarization and processing documents for them. In the end, he said that he would make it a point to return to her within three weeks.

Gertrude made contact with Klaus delivering a message from Horst. "For a long and extended time, we have been worried about this with Peter," said Klaus. They both continued to talk, and returned to each other, with the agreement to meet again in three weeks.

One day Klaus was summoned to the camp commander's office. The commander liked Klaus; he protected him as best he could.

At this time, Klaus made only minor improvements in the barracks with Peter and several prisoners. The Germans knew that the approaching front would force them to close the camp and did not want to spend money on major renovations. From now on supervision over the repair of the barracks passed into the hands of an officer sent from the High Command Headquarters in Berlin. To protect him the commander released Klaus from his position. "What would you like to do?" asked the commander.

Klaus surprised by this question, thought about this for a moment and said, "I heard that they would take dead prisoners outside the camp to bury them. Sir, I would like to ask to be assigned to this group. I would like to be a driver of a truck."

"Done," said the commander.

"Sir, I have one final request," said Klaus.

"Yes, what is it?" asked the commander.

"Working with me is one prisoner; he is also a German and was forcibly conscripted into the Soviet army of Lithuania. He has been working with me for a long time. Will you delegate him to the same group? He has a strong back. He can load dead bodies of the prisoners into the trucks, efficiently," said Klaus.

The commander listened carefully to Klaus' words. Then he looked at Klaus and said, "You were here from the beginning with me and I like you. You've been a diligent German. If you like him, as I like you, then I will certainly direct him to join the group. What is the individuals name in question?"

"Matas Zukas," said Klaus.

The commander recorded the name in his notebook and said, "In two days you will move into barrack no.7. You will be at Sergeant Kramer's disposal, there. You are now free." Klaus then left the office.

Klaus and Peter checked in at barrack no.7. Sergeant Kramer had two trucks, with two drivers; four German soldiers for grading and twelve additional prisoners who were to dig pits in the woods to bury the dead bodies. One of the drivers was Klaus. Three days later, two trucks left the camp. Six prisoners and three Germans soldiers were driving, in each truck. The prisoners were sitting in front of the truck and two of the soldiers in the rear, a safe distance away from the other prisoners. One German soldier drove with Klaus. In the forest, the prisoners dug a deep pit to bury as many as twenty bodies. The work was difficult and hazardous. After four hours they all returned to the camp.

The next day a truck exited the camp loaded with the corpses of another 13 dead prisoners. There were four prisoners for unloading and two Germans to guard the prisoners. The bodies were lowered down into the cold damp earth. They completely filled the pit, with earth. Klaus found himself again, driving a truck; Peter was then assigned to throw the additional bodies into the pit to bury them. He had a strong constitution, and he didn't get tired easily. He dug the graves. He saw himself as a nameless, towering figure hovering above the detail; as a delivering angel, desperate to finish his task.

One day Gertrude came to the Stalag 18 camp and wanted to see Klaus. She had not obtained the proper clearance permission in advance to see him. "I want to talk to the commander," said Gertrude. The soldier made a phone call to the commander's office. Gertrude was only allowed to enter the building and wait there. Rules and endless protocol must be followed.

After fifteen minutes there appeared a tormented Klaus. Gertrude noticed Klaus's nervous behavior. "When last we saw each other, our relationship completely changed," he said quietly. Klaus then told Gertrude what they were doing. "Tell this to Horst," added Klaus.

"Five minutes have passed," said the soldier. Klaus and Gertrude parted with disappointment and tears in their eyes. Not knowing when they would see each other again; if ever. An enigma, covering a layer of secrets.

When Horst arrived at Gertrude's home, he found her very upset and melancholy. Gertrude then explained to Horst everything that Klaus and Peter were doing. "We need to act as quickly as possible."

"What do you mean?" asked Gertrude.

"You'll find out the secret in time," said Horst. "I will arrive here again in approximately two weeks. Be ready", said Horst as he hurriedly left Gertrude's home. Unfortunately, she did not have a complete understanding of why Horst said, "Be ready." The unanswered questions tormented her mind.

Horst spent a week of preparation and settling important matters. After ten additional days; he arrived at his home and spoke to Mary of everything he understood from his perspective; of what he, could remember. In the end, Horst said, "We are leaving. I am tired and closing the factory. There's nothing here now for me anymore. When the Russians arrive here they will loot, pillage and burn, taking everything. Remember to pack only what you need, only the most necessary things. In two days; we will leave this place, forever." Mary was very concerned and remained silent trying to deny what was happening. She now had no alternative but to trust Horst.

Chapter XII
Goodbye to Friends

HORST HANDED OVER THE FACTORY to the foreman, a former friend. Horst said he was going to Germany to visit his first cousin; he hid the real intention. Now, Horst had more important responsibilities; other than the factory. He was committed to saving the life of Peter and Klaus. No one understood what Horst was planning. He kept the secret of his intentions hidden deep within his mind as a secret buried deep within the chasm of his subconscious.

After three days Horst dispatched Mary, John, and Vladek into the waiting car. He drove up to his factory. The gate was locked so the vehicle stopped. He got out of the car. Horst stood for a moment in stoic silence. The factory was his past life. He saw his old friend to whom he worked with and trusted, in the factory; he waved to him and drove off.

On the way, Horst told Mary that they were all going to the city of Olsztyn. "To Olsztyn?" said Mary, who was surprised.

"Do not be afraid. Everything is prepared and taken care of. You will later learn, and realize when you see clearly at the right moment." Finally, after 4 hours of driving, they reached the signpost of their goal, Olsztyn. Horst had a friend with whom Mary had previously visited. Mary had stopped there many times with the children. The next day Horst arose in the morning well before sunrise and drove away. Where was he going? No one knew.

It had been two weeks since Gertrude last saw Klaus. It was a rainy day at the end of October 1943. Klaus and Peter were working together to expedite the disposal of bodies from the camp three times a week. The forest was a mile away from the camp. It was overcast and there was yet another storm on the horizon. The Germans did not want to go into the forest; however, they had to execute the order. There were only ten bodies to be liquidated. To quickly handle this burden, the Germans abducted four prisoners who were to discharge and bury the bodies.

When they arrived in the woods, Klaus stepped down from the truck and made a quick effort with the prisoners to throw requisitioned dead bodies into the pit. Then they grabbed the shovels and began to fill the hole with dirt. The Germans were smoking cigarettes. They stood by the truck shielding them from the rain. There was a huge storm, on the horizon with thunder and lighting. A series of machine gun bursts were heard. The Germans, surprised, were caught off guard. Two Germans were killed instantly. Then there was a second short burst of machine guns. A third German shot two prisoners accidentally, before he was shot by the overzealous civilians. Hearing the volley of shots, Peter and Klaus fell to the ground in a panic. Peter, Klaus, and the other prisoner were fortunate that the bullets did not reach them.

Four men dressed in civilian clothes jumped out from the woods. Two men came to Peter and Klaus and told them to pull off their shirts. Both of them did immediately. "Now quickly remove the shirts from these two bullet-ridden prisoners and put them on. Each of you, change your shirt with one of them," said one of the men. Peter and Klaus quickly did so, without complaining. When they finished; they willingly went along with the other men. One of the men shot two of the bodies to make holes in the shirts. The fourth prisoner was lying on the ground.

One of the men in Russian said, "Run!" Without waiting, the surprised prisoner began to flee into the forest in a panic. The goal on everyone's mind was to save his life. Klaus and Peter with the other men started walking into the dark forest. Everything occurred in five minutes.

After about a hundred meters, they all loaded into a small truck and left. Peter and Klaus sat in somber silence not knowing what to say. "It's raining again," one of the men said in Polish.

"The Germans were completely surprised. Now, there will be no trace of us. The rain will wash away the tracks," said the second man. They rode through the forest, often changing directions. After half an hour they reached the edge of a small village. When they stopped, Peter and Klaus got out of the small truck.

Excitedly, everyone went home. "Undress," said one of the men. In the middle of the room were a series of round tubs with warm water. Peter and Klaus removed their bloodied clothes and started to wash themselves. After five minutes they were washed. After twenty minutes, they were neatly shaved and dressed in fresh clothes; after half an hour they were again driving in a car far away from the camp.

Peter and Klaus were in disbelief, in shock. They did not know exactly what was happening. One of the men, who rescued them, gave them a word of basic delivery instructions. Peter and Klaus performed, amicably in their tasks. The driver did not say a word. He just handed them the imported notarized documents. When Peter opened his document, he saw the signature and name of Peter Krause. Klaus was called Klaus Schroder. "We have to memorize our new names and identities," said Klaus. In addition, they had requisitioned official papers that they were going to Olsztyn, for general business matters. They rode in silence for two hours. The rain fell unceasingly and stopped when they reached Olsztyn.

After an hour the Nazis noticed that one convoy truck had not returned to the camp. In response, an alarm was raised and a truck loaded with twenty soldiers and two field survey trucks set out into the deep forest. When they arrived at the burial place in the forest they saw fresh bodies of three Germans laid where they were killed with two prisoners of war. The faces of the Germans and prisoners were beaten, contorted, bruised, malformed and completely unrecognizable as a final insult signature, they were riddled with bullets. The soldiers were searching for some pleasure, to victimize. It was wet, miserable and the Nazis searched and found nothing. They loaded the bodies into a convoy truck and returned to the camp.

Schneider, the commander of the camp was waiting in his office for the news. One of the officers prepared a complete list of the casualties, to the commander. "Do you have the names of those who died?" asked the commandant, Schneider.

"Yes," replied the officer and listed the names only of the German soldiers. He also gave numbers of two prisoners who died there, the names of Klaus and Matas. Three prisoners escaped because their bodies were not found.

He gave the order, "Tomorrow, search the forest! Take the dogs and comb the forest. Punish the guilty," the commander said. When the officer came out, the commander said to himself, "I do feel sorry for all those soldiers, who died so needlessly and Klaus, I did like him."

Chapter XIII
Parting

HORST, WITH MARY AND THE children, lived with Hans. Two additional weeks had passed then Horst invited Gertrude to dinner. The dinner was today, on Tuesday and Gertrude did not know that Mary was with her children in Olsztyn. Horst kept his past history a secret. Gertrude was surprised when she saw Mary. They embraced each other and cried it was a very emotional introduction and a tearful reunion.

There at the long table sat the owner of the house Hans, along with Horst, Mary, her children John and Vladek and Gertrude. Horst was nervous all too frequently. He could not find rest within himself. Peace was a memory too far away. He continued to listen in contemplation, looking nervously out the window. The family was wondering, what was his motive? Horst remained mysterious.

A car pulled up in the driveway. Horst jumped from his chair and again walked to the window. He smiled, mischievously, and joyously said, "I promise, I have an amazing surprise for you all. Stay here and I'll come again, soon." Then he left the living room and went outside.

After a few minutes, the door opened and Horst came in weeping. Behind him came Peter and later Klaus. Mary and Gertrude were surprised, stood to their feet, and ran quickly to their respective husbands. Mary ran to Peter, who was overcome with emotion, kissing him and hugging him tenderly. Peter was elated; he embraced Mary, holding her. He tried to remember her face. He slowly recalled exactly who she was. Klaus had described her features. The same thing was done by Gertrude and Klaus. The last time she saw him; it was three weeks ago, under different circumstances. Now they were free!

Mary released Peter from her embrace and called out, "John, Vladek, it's your father!" They both ran happily to him. Peter fell down on his knees and threw his arms around them, happily. There was extraordinary elation. Horst and Hans were stepping out watching the reunion between the families. Both men were ecstatic, crying with happiness.

Peter sat with Mary and the children. Gertrude sat next to Klaus. Horst raised a bottle of champagne and poured it into prepared glasses. He made an important and historic toast, "Let's drink, to our health, blessing and to the completion of our separation from our enemies! Freedom!"

Everyone happily drank the champagne. "May we also drink the vodka?" asked Vladek, who was one year older than John. Everyone at the table laughed at that question.

"You have all the time in the world for that," said Mary.

Horst asked Hans to take John and Vladek into the kitchen and to keep them playfully occupied. He understood the meaning of this request; what followed was a very serious conversation. Hans retrieved the children and went into an adjoining room. Horst did not want to expose anyone to danger. The children were innocent and should only know what they have been instructed by Mary. Horst said, "I'm relieved that you escaped from the camp. It was a very difficult time for you all to deal with. It cost you everything including your lives. You are free!"

He then recalled the account of how it was done. "We chose a rainy and stormy day. We hired men who had knowledge of that forest, and knew the German's schedule for disposing the bodies. Do not worry, Germans will not come looking for you. You were instructed in a timely and quick manner to exchange shirts and clothing with the deceased prisoners. So according to the Germans, you both appear to be dead. All went according to our conceived plans. We then had to develop a plan to escape. The men's knowledge about the forest and the rain ensured, that the Germans could not follow or see how the cars escaped or that there was an escape at all. All that was left was to clean you up and make you presentable with new identities."

"The situation with the German army was hopeless. England and America joined the war to defeat the Germans. We could not continue to live within German occupation. The Russians would take everything including our lives. I had all my savings in a Swiss bank; more than enough money for everyone, in this room. I was committed to go to Switzerland and then to America. This is a very difficult situation. The Germans are working with the secret police, the Gestapo. I had to secretly withhold information to accomplish this goal. I was told the decision belongs to you. Let's first listen to what Klaus and Peter have to say; before other decisions will be made." Horst concluded.

The families sat up late, listening to Klaus and Peter. Mary felt respect and an obligation toward Peter and said, "Together we will rebuild your memories and your life my dear friend." She kissed Peter on the cheek. Gertrude knew that Klaus could not continue to live in their home in Olsztyn. The house was no longer a safe haven for them. It was known, what the Germans would do to retaliate. Did they come to the conclusion that Klaus was truly dead? They did not want to know the answer to this, at this time. Horst suggested that everyone go to bed and think over the whole situation.

The next day, they arose refreshed, and in an optimistic mood. Mary and Gertrude prepared eggs and black coffee for breakfast. The men sat in the dining room reflecting about the situation which they found themselves in. Breakfast was served. Peter and Klaus could not remember when they last ate scrambled eggs with bacon. They laughed at their appetite. Hans in accordance with the agreement lifted John and Vladek and took them into the next room, where they played with various toys.

Horst began to say, "We have so little time, and we must decide what to do with the rest of our lives. What did you finally decide?" There was only silence. Horst looked once at Klaus, and again at Peter. Klaus was the first to speak. "Gertrude and I do not have a choice. Fortunately, we do not have children and it is far easier for us to make a decision. We're moving with you, Horst. If we stay here, the Russians will surely find out that I was working in the camp. Although, I was sent there to be punished; they would not interrupt what the Germans were doing. If they knew what I understood about Germany; the enemies would surely kill me. We then have no other choice. We're leaving."

All eyes were then turned to Peter and Mary. Peter announced, "We are staying in Poland." Mary, lying in bed with Peter, at night confided with him telling him the account in detail. "I have discussed this a long time with Mary. This is our decision today." Horst tried to divert the conversation from this final decision, but without success. "We have two small children and a house in Poland. Also, it is known that within days the Russians are coming and this will be a difficult time and season. I want to see if the house remains standing. I believe the Germans are still living in our house," stated Peter.

"Later, we will make the final decision of where our family will go," said Peter.

"You and the children will have no future here. Peter, if you lose your life, Mary, what will you do then?" asked Horst.

Klaus, who was sitting in silence said, "I was with Peter in the camp and I know the difficult labor and effort he has put into his own recovery, to regain his memory with the hope of reuniting with his family. I have spoken to Peter of all I know about forgotten events with his family. He could not wait to see them. They are together now. They have decided to stay in Poland. Is this the right decision? Time will answer this difficult question. Peter, we respect your final decision. We will stand with you, in whatever you decide. We will all miss you. If you want to see your home again, then, I'm going with you."

Hans had a small shop in which he was selling sundries, dry goods and clothing. Hans arranged the papers for Klaus and Peter; that they were going to buy goods in the store. The protocol was then legally handled by Horst, who had a sufficient knowledge and Peter knew very well that he had to be shrewd. Peter and Klaus departed early in the morning. The German patrol stopped them just before Olsztyn. Klaus and Peter gave the Nazis papers and waited, impatiently. Their hearts responded and beat like base drums. They could not show any outward signs of fear. They learned firsthand of activities in the camp, witnessing how the Nazis inflicted torture on prisoners of war. They in earnest were calm and spoke to them fluently in German. "All right," said the German, who handed over the documents to them. Escaping, they saw many trucks filled with a host of German soldiers. In twenty minutes they reached their destination, Charles' house.

Peter got out of the car and walked to the door. He knocked loudly. There was no answer. He knocked again; silence. Peter returned to the car and said to Klaus, "There are no people in the house. We'll be back later."

"Where are we going to go now?" asked Klaus.

"We're going to see the house," said Peter.

"Lead me on, I simply do not remember the details about this," said Klaus.

"You know, I'm trying to remember details too," said Peter.

"It will be best for all of us to wait for Charles. He will direct us in the way we should go," said Klaus "If we draw attention to ourselves by running away now it may be obvious to the Germans. Here is a pub. Let's go in and order a cup of coffee and have some vodka."

Peter and Klaus were sitting in the pub, discussing for about an hour, where they were drinking coffee and "chasing it" with a glass of vodka. Klaus paid the bill right before they left. They got into their vehicle and drove to the house of Charles. The lights were on. Peter came up to the door and knocked, thinking, "How will I recognize him? I simply do not remember him."

The door opened, and a tall man stood in the doorway. Peter stood motionless waiting to see Charles' reaction. "Peter?" said Charles, who was surprised, as he playfully pulled him into the hallway; embracing him warmly.

"I'm not alone. I'm with Klaus," said Peter. Charles opened the door and waved his hand for Klaus to enter the house.

Later, everyone was sitting at the table drinking vodka and black coffee prepared by Sophia, Charles' wife. Peter said he had come to see him and his house. "Your home is fine. The entire street is occupied by Germans," said Charles.

"I would like to see it," said Peter.

"In the morning I will go to work and I finish at three, then we will go there," said Charles who continued, "The city is full of Germans. We must be steadfast." They sat for a long time listening to Peter and Klaus' stories. Charles and his wife were elated with happiness that Peter was becoming reacquainted with his family.

The following day, Peter and Klaus waited for Charles to return from work. He worked in the bakery. There was never a shortage of bread in his house. Charles led them by the network of side streets. They crossed the bridge on the river Vistula and after five minutes they were on East Street. They drove slowly. "This is your house," said Charles; pointing his finger at the brick, two-story house.

Peter looked at him, carefully. He did not remember when he built the brick and mortar home. But he knew important details from Mary. "I built it," he said aloud.

"Now, I know what you're experiencing," said Klaus. He knew why Peter did not want to go with them.

"Can we go downtown? I would like to walk the streets. I'll remember details by association," said Peter. Klaus agreed and Charles drove them along the side streets into the downtown area.

It was already after five and the sky slowly darkened as the Sun went down. Peter and Klaus got out of the car and walked down the sidewalk. Peter looked around to familiarize, himself with this street. He said, "There was a store with clothing behind the corner." When they reached the corner, he turned left. Beyond twenty yards there was actually, a small clothing store.

A black car drove past them. Charles was walking behind a short distance; he noticed how the black car slowed and the German officer behind the wheel looked back at Peter and Klaus. The officer turned onto the first street that he came to.

Charles approached Peter, who related what he observed. Klaus and Peter then turned back on the street and walked toward the car. The black car came up and stopped behind them and a stout German got out of it. Peter and Klaus noticed him, and turned into the nearest door, of a building. This door led to a small courtyard between the buildings. They had their notarized

German documents but, they could not risk being exposed. They were subject to multiple checkpoints here in the city. They then heard, the sound of footsteps walking far behind them. Peter and Klaus quickly entered the small courtyard through the two doors. They found out in horror that the courtyard was closed. They were trapped. Klaus had hidden in a niche, in the wall.

Peter heard the voice of the German who strongly said, "Stop! Hands up! I'll shoot!" He walked with a gun in his hand in the direction of Peter. Peter lifted his hands and stood motionless absolutely still.

Peter for a moment thought, "Have I carelessly lost my possession?"

The German came within a measured distance to Peter and looking around cautiously and said, "Do we know each other; from somewhere? I have an excellent memory. You are Peter Mayer are you not?"

Peter stiffened and said, "No. My name is Krause."

"Come closer and show me your papers," demanded the German, standing; in the crossing between the buildings.

"How could he remember me? Who is he?" Peter asked himself.

"I'm Shultz," proudly announced the German. Peter did not remember that name. Shultz pulled out his left hand toward Peter; and in his right hand a gun was pointing, directly at Peter. Peter handed him the important papers. Shultz opened them carefully and read Peter Krause. "Oh, I see you changed your name. You ran away once before from me, but not this time,"

Shultz said. Now, Peter remembered the echoes of those words. Mary mentioned that Peter escaped from home. He refused to sign the "list of cooperation" with the Nazis.

A window was closed on the third floor above them. Shultz raised his head upward. Klaus was just waiting for this opportunity. He was hidden in a small niche in the wall of the building that was invisible to the German. Klaus jumped up behind his intended victim and stabbed Shultz in the back. With his other hand, he covered the Germans mouth so that he would not give a shout. Klaus pulled out the knife and stabbed the German again, in the heart to be absolutely sure he was deprived of his life. Shultz slumped to the ground. Peter quickly retrieved his document from Schultz's hand. "We're leaving," said Klaus as they quickly ran toward the door that led to the courtyard. Peter cautiously opened the door and looked around. Life outside the building continuously moved at a frenetic pace.

Charles standing on the other side of the street was very scared. He gave a sign to get out, quickly. Peter came out first; Klaus closed the door behind him. They walked quickly toward the vehicle. When they rounded the corner, the men began to run for a moment, believing the enemy was on that short street. The street was unoccupied. They turned onto another side street where a car was parked. They were walking deliberately. There were several people in the vicinity of the vehicle. Klaus opened the door and they got inside the car. They drove on the road, in silence. Only when they later crossed the bridge on the Vistula River, Charles asked, "What happened there?"

"We killed a German," replied Peter. They then continued to drive in silence.

When the car stopped in front of the house, Charles said, "Let us agree, that at home; we don't say a word… of what happened." They all went home and took off their jackets and sat down at the table.

Sophia served dinner and asked, "How was everything?"

Charles looked at Peter and Klaus and said, "All right. The house is well maintained. We were in a bar and drank vodka and we came home."

During the dinner, they discussed what to do next. "Tomorrow, we will take bread from the bakery and return to Olsztyn," said Klaus. When Sophia went to bed, Charles, Peter, and Klaus were sitting up late at night discussing what had happened.

"Why did I come here?" exclaimed Peter, who blamed the current events on himself.

Klaus looked at Peter and said, "Do not blame yourself. It is now late; it is time to go to sleep."

In the morning they all arose, drank coffee and went with Charles to the bakery. They paid for 50 loaves of bread and loaded them into the car. Peter and Klaus said their goodbyes to Charles and drove back to Olsztyn.

Peter was shocked at all the events that happened and confronted Klaus, "You saved my life again. You killed a man for me. I will remember this for the rest of my life. Let's agree, not to say anything to Mary about what happened." Everything was fine on the trip back. In the afternoon they arrived in Olsztyn.

They both greeted their families and then spoke in private with Horst. Horst said, "It's now time, to make the final decision. We must take the bread and deliver it to Hans' shop, and return home." Peter and Mary put on their coats and went outside, to speak in private. A half hour passed; and they came back, and sat down with everyone at the table.

Horst looked at Peter and Mary and asked, "What decision did you make?"

"We have decided to stay," said Peter.

"Oh, no," said Horst.

"Horst, we have two children. Mary does not want to leave," said Peter.

"I will respect your decision," said Horst who asked, "Where are you planning to stay?"

"We do not know. We have to look for a safe haven," said Peter.

"I'll speak to Hans to see if you can stay here temporarily," said Horst. He then added, "We're leaving in approximately two days."

Mary and Gertrude were upset that they would be separated. Horst talked with Hans about Peter and Mary's situation. "They can live here as long as is necessary. They will be safe here," said Hans.

It was now October of 1943. Horst had prepared all the necessary documents for himself, Klaus and Gertrude. "We now go into the unknown. I do not know what will happen in the future. We plan to go to Krakow and from there to Vienna. I have friends. We will want to go to Zurich. I have a cousin in the United States of America. My friend, I do not know if we will ever meet again. I wish you all success and happy travels," said Horst. They all cried. Who made the correct decision, no one knew.

In the end, Horst approached Peter, paused and said, "I'm sorry for the fateful events that happened to you. Frederic was a good man," and embraced Peter. Horst, Gertrude, and Klaus then left the house and entered into the vehicle, and drove away. Hans, Peter, and Mary with their children were emotional. They watched the car drive away and vanish around the corner.

Chapter XIV
Survival

PETER WORKED IN THE SHOP TOGETHER with Hans and Mary. Mary was a responsible homemaker and mother to John and Vladek. She taught them Polish and German in her free time. In order not to expose Peter to danger, Hans handled all outside matters. The war continued in the Eastern bloc where the Russians pushed the Germans toward the Polish territory. The German occupation was losing ground on all fronts. The situation was very tenuous with Germany. Germany did not spare the outside disposable population of the conquered countries. The arrests, mass shootings, and taking of the conquered victims to concentration camps continued. Liquidation was the primary agenda of the Nazis.

Hans knew that the Germans would withdraw territorially; he would have to leave the house and the shop and run. Retaliation of the Russians was horrific in the areas already liberated. There was a malicious confiscation of possessions and personal property of the German people of which they now possessed. Civilians were marched out and shot or deported to labor camps.

On the advice of Horst, Hans placed the currencies in Swiss bank accounts. Switzerland was neutral and the only secure place, to deposit their savings. Hans's wife died and his son was killed in the First World War. All of his other close family members by this time in the war were lost or had fled for safety. Hans did not have anyone and had no further place to run. He had said many times, "I am tired of life. What is left for me? There remains only for me to die." Hans was 82 years old. He was glad Peter and Mary were not captured by the Germans. He trusted them completely. Trust was a commitment, a loyalty, which could not be broken within a lifetime.

Two additional weeks passed, Hans received a letter from Horst, "We are now in Krakow. See you soon." It was a prearranged sign that everything was in order. In the evening, everyone was sitting near the stove in their home. They were warming their hands because the supply of coal was limited. They burned it only in the evening. Hans's house was in the suburbs. The property had many acres of land with an enormous forest near the house. Peter cut a few trees and chopped them into pieces so that the wood from the acreage could be gathered and burned in the winter.

A month had passed since Horst, Klaus and Gertrude left. Hans was impatient with the long silence. In the evening, sitting by the stove, he said, "I hope that nothing serious has happened to them."

Mary asked Peter, "What ended up happening to Andrew? You did not mention him in your story."

Peter looked at Mary and asked, "Andrew who?"

"Andrew Miller," answered Mary. She immediately understood Peter's difficulty. Mary spoke about the story of their friendship and added, "He went with you to Olsztyn at that time."

Peter sat in silence and tried to recall one single detail of those events. After a long pause, he said, "It seems to me that he is dead."

Mary looked at Peter with deep emotion in her eyes and added, "He was a good friend."

The next day, Peter awoke early in the morning; he was anxious and sat on his bed. 'What happened?" asked Mary, who was frightened.

"I was thinking all night about Andrew. I know the truth about what happened there in the dugout," said Peter.

"In what dugout?" asked Mary. Peter then dressed and went to the kitchen. He added the wood to the stove and boiled water for black coffee. Mary came into the kitchen and started talking and sipping the black coffee. The coffee helped to calm her.

He told her the history of what he remembered. "Shortly before Andrew died he gave me a map, which had marked the location where hidden cash and currency were buried in the ground. The ground was his parent's grave. Andrew told me to understand the gravity of the situation."

Time passed quickly. It was now 1944. Hans had not received any messages from Horst. Peter helped in the bakery. Mary ran the affairs of the house. The Russian troops were approaching Lithuania and Belarus. By June of 1944, the Germans troops suffered heavy losses and the Russians were inching closer to Poland. Peter, shocked and surprised, realized the truth. His extended family would ultimately, have to flee from Olsztyn. Peter visited Charles several times and always asked about his house. His dream was to simply return to his home when the Germans left the occupation in the area. Driving on the roads was dangerous. German armies were preparing their line of defense.

In January 1945, Peter and Mary ultimately decided to flee from Olsztyn. Hans wanted to stay. Peter persuaded him to escape with his family. Hans decided to stay with Peter and Mary. He said, "Where you go, I will go. I do not have a real family other than you." The Russians were literally outside the doors. Peter, with his extended family, packed the most important items along with food into the car and together with Hans began to drive to Charles' home. Hans cried many tears when he left his home and shop.

It was winter. The road was overrun with the German army and refugees. Few people drove automobiles; others traveled on foot pulling small carts with personal belongings; and others just walked on foot with no personal belongings, just trying to save their lives. This time Peter drove six hours to reach Charles' home. Charles prepared everything for them in advance.

The following day Peter and Hans went to see what was going on with the house. When they entered the street, they noticed the Germans marching within the area. They drove to Peter's house. They entered the yard. Peter got out of the vehicle and approached the door. He pushed slightly, opening the door and said, "Hello. Hello. Is anybody in here?" Peter's heart began to beat louder. He slowly stepped inside the house. After a moment, he went out and said to Hans, "Hans. They moved out. The house is ours," and invited Hans inside his house. He showed him the whole house. The Germans, who lived previously here, surprisingly maintained the care of the house. The walls were painted and they placed new furniture. After a moment, Peter said, "We're going to Mary and move in here, immediately."

Peter arrived home. He entered the kitchen and excitedly said, "The occupant has moved out. The house is completely empty. We're going there at once." Mary wept with happiness. They thanked Charles and Sophia for their hospitality. They gathered the things that they brought with them; and loaded them into the car and quickly drove off to his home, with the children and Hans.

Mary could not restrain her tears of happiness. It's been over four years since they left the house. They pulled into the yard and went out of the car. Mary entered the house. Behind her followed John and Vladek. They stood in the kitchen. Mary said to the children, "This is your home. You were born here," and hugged them. John was now six, and Vladek seven. Mary looked at every corner of the house. She went down to the basement. There were rough repairs made to the wall and foundation of the demolished section that was caused by a grenade explosion. There was as yet no electricity in the house.

Peter and Hans unloaded the car and placed everything inside the house. They looked for a candle; Peter found one in the cabinet locker in the corridor. He then lit the candle and said, "Boys come with me to the shed. We must find some wood for the stove; it is brutally cold." Snow had fallen outside; it was an ankle deep. John and Vladek followed the footsteps of their father.

In the shed, they found coal and a supply of old boards. Peter gave a few small boards to the children. The children carried them to the kitchen. Peter found an old bucket and loaded it with coal, and carried it inside the house. The fire in the stove brought heat inside the kitchen within 15 minutes. Everyone was sitting in front of a burning candle. "Finally with great relief we are home," said Mary.

Chapter XV
A Real Tragedy

MARY SURVEYED THE PROPERTY. She knew every angle. She went outside to the courtyard and looked to the right and then to the left to see if she could see the old neighbors. Someone was outside at the end of the street. "That's probably Irena," she thought.

Peter said, "I am going to the bakery to speak to Charles. Maybe, they need someone to work there?" He had to drive there.

When he was near the bakery a German patrol stopped him and ordered him to get out of the car. "We are requisitioning this vehicle," said one of the Nazis as he pushed Peter aside. Peter tried to protest, speaking in German. A German needs this car. "Soon the Russians will come here; they will confiscate your property from you," said one of the Nazis, as they boasted together with his colleagues. Then they quickly drove away with their vehicle.

Peter had no option, but to walk to the bakery. The owner of the bakery had just bought the flour. The citizens needed to have bread. Meat was in short supply. Bread was a necessity. Peter asked for a job in the bakery but in those hard times, the owner had only two helpers. One of them was Charles. He spoke to Charles, telling him what happened to the car.

"It's a shame. The Germans are requisitioning possessions, nothing will be overlooked," said Charles.

Peter bought three loaves of bread and said, "We'll meet again in two days." He left and walked home.

Peter came home dead tired. It took him over an hour to walk home from the bakery. When he entered the kitchen, Mary asked, "I did not hear your car. What happened?"

Peter replied, "The Germans requisitioned it." Mary started to cry.

Hans heard these words and then cursed the dreaded Nazis, "They take our belongings. My car served me many years; now we must all walk on foot; I am old. My body is tired."

The city of Olsztyn was captured and the eastern front moved near the town where Peter lived with his family. Fighting between the German and Russian forces was greatly intensified. The offensive was moving ever closer to a place near the suburbs of the city. Russian aircraft bombarded German positions. The explosions of artillery and missiles were overhead. They were sitting in the kitchen. There were many dangerous moments when the house was shaking violently.

Hans, relaxing in a kitchen chair, then said to Peter, "Peter. Thank you for your assistance. Especially for those two years spent with you. Life has made little sense to me. The worst is coming. I have no home anymore; I have become old and tired. When I survive this war I would like to live with you; until the end of my days. If I do not survive, here are all the documents that you will need to prove that everything of importance is yours."

He then handed the file to Peter. "I have given everything to you, the house, the land, and money in the bank. I feel like I am living a bad dream, and I can't wake up."

"Hans, what are you talking about? Everything will be fine. We only need to survive these next few days as the Russians will surely come. We do not know what to expect. We are living in horrible times. We have to remain together," said Peter. Then he finally shook the hand of Hans.

The Russian bombing of Nazi posts would intensify each morning. The sound of explosions and missiles were shaking the windows in the house. Those gathered in the house were now sitting in the basement. Airplanes on both sides flew over their heads and more bombs were dropped over the artillery's battlefields. Vladek asked, "I have never seen a plane that close. Can I see them?"

"Absolutely not," said Mary. "Now is the season of war."

Minute to minute shots rang out and were heard closer and closer to the home. They heard several explosions approaching the house. The house was shaking and the dust was falling from the ceiling into the basement. Outside, there were single shots fired as well as rapid bursts of shots from machine guns. They could hear yelling in German and running as shots were fired. "They are retreating," said Peter. Next to the building grenades echoed, shaking the house. The firing began again and then a break. There was empty silence.

After ten minutes, an unknown soldier opened the door to the house. A Russian dialect was heard. The family was huddled in the corner of the basement. Peter embraced Mary. Mary, on the other hand, was holding Vladek and John in her arms. Adjacent to Mary, sat Hans crouching down. The house was entirely dark. A soldier went down the stairs to the basement. When the footsteps stopped; the soldier asked in Russian, "Is anyone here?"

Peter was beside himself. He asked himself, "Speak or remain silent?" He had to make a quick decision. "If I do not answer and they find my family here, who knows what will happen." After a few seconds, his answer came; he spoke in Russian, "Yes. I'm here with my whole family."

"Get out," said the soldier, and then he backed up. Peter and Mary held hands with their frightened children, and along with Hans they left the basement.

In the hallway, two Russian soldiers stood with their rifles pointed at them ready to fire. "Is anyone else here?" asked the soldier.

"There is no one," answered Peter, tightly embracing his whole family.

The soldiers looked at each other and one of them impulsively, asked, "Do you have anything to eat?"

"There, in the locker," said Peter pointing his finger. The soldier went to the locker opened it and pulled out a loaf of bread with a little lard. "That's all we have. We have not left the house for two days because of the turmoil," said Peter in Russian.

The soldier looked at the children broke a piece of bread divided it into two parts and handed it to Vladek and John and said, "They must eat. You can starve." The rest of the bread was divided into two portions. One portion he kept for himself and the second was given to his colleague. The Russian drew a knife and retrieved the lard from another jar and put a large portion of it on the loaf and handed it to his friend. They both ate and were satisfied. There was silence. "Do you have something to drink?" asked the Russian.

"Water is in the kitchen, in the jug," Peter replied. One of the Russians went into the kitchen and came back with a pitcher and two glasses. He poured water into a glass and handed it to his colleague.

After they ate and drank, they looked at them and said, "Thank you," in their dialect and they left. Everyone breathed a sigh of relief.

They were only a portion of the patrol. Later that day, a large number of soldiers surveyed the street. Peter would not let his family leave the house. In the morning, Peter looked out the window. There was silence. He walked into the corridor; opened the door to the yard, and went outside. No one was there. Behind him entered Hans. The shed standing outside was completely destroyed. The adjoining neighbor's house was in ruins. There was a light snow on the ground. The constant outbreak of artillery missiles and grenades left the area leveled, and desolate.

After a moment Mary walked into the scene with Vladek and John. They sat secretly in the basement for two long days. "The fresh air outside will do us good," said Mary. Peter checked the perimeter of the house. A few cracked and broken windows filled out the landscape with explosions and debris.

"I hid the food in the shed. The soldiers would have taken everything from us," said Peter then he walked over to the shed.

He began to throw away the discards; pieces of boards. Hans helped him as he was able. Mary came into the house. John and Vladek watched as their father and Hans cleared additional wreckage.

From the ruins of the shed jumped out a frightened cat. "Cat!" shouted Vladek and together with John ran after him. Hans tried to stop them. They ran past him.

"Halt!" shouted Peter! He did not finish screaming "Stop," another shaking of powerful explosions shook the ground. Pieces of earth were throwing debris into the air. The force of the explosions knocked Peter to the ground. Mary heard the tumult and ran out of the house, into the backyard. She saw Peter lying on the ground. Hans was near him, lying face down on the ground. A few steps away, the children; John and Vladek cowered terrified in a big hole. Mary screamed, "Oh, no!" and she ran to the children. Mary dropped to her knees and first turned to John, who was face down on the ground and not moving. Blood was pouring from his mouth. He was bruised. John did not have a left hand. He was dead.

She cursed Vladek, who was lying on his side. Vladek's left leg was missing. He gave shallow signs of life. Mary touched him and screamed, "Vladek...Vladek! How did this happen?" Mary desperately screamed, "Why did I leave them alone?" Mary was in shock, in disbelief failing to understand why they were dead. Mary held their lifeless bodies. She did not acknowledge that the children were indeed dead.

After a few minutes, Mary reached Peter. Peter was breathing heavily. He was unconscious. On her knees, Mary approached Hans, who was now lying face down. Mary touched him and said, "Don't die Hans. Please hang on. Stay with us. Stay alive." In a matter of minutes, Hans was dead. "Why did this happen?" Mary screamed desperately. Surrounding her was the silence of not a living soul. The neighbors heard the explosions and were terrified to leave their homes. Mary checked Peter again. Peter lay motionless. She began to move him and began calling out, "Get up! Wake up, children! Get up! Do not die. Only you must remain with me." Mary arose from her knees and ran over to John. She took him in her arms; and laid him down near Hans. Mary did the same with Vladek.

It was fifteen minutes before Peter slowly opened his eyes and saw Mary's weeping face. There was pounding in his ears with pain in his head. Peter was confused. He did not know where he was. Twice before, he found himself recovering with the same concussion. When he stood on his feet, he looked around and asked, "What happened?" Mary did not speak. "Where are my children? Where is Hans?" Mary pointed her hands in the direction of the children. Peter looked up and saw three bloody bodies lying on the ground. Peter took a few steps in their direction and fell to his knees. "Oh, my God…No!" He cried in a loud voice, "Oh. No! John, Vladek," Mary knelt beside him and embraced the bodies of their children. John and Vladek lay alongside old Hans. "Why did he die, and not me?" shouted Peter. Peter brought the children's bodies back home. He put John, Vladek, and Hans on the big bed. Mary and Peter pulled off the bloodied clothes of John and Vladek and washed their scared bodies. Later they dressed them in clean clothes. They did the same with Hans. They both did this reverently, almost in silence.

When the preparations were finished they knelt near the bed where the bodies were laid out and began to pray.

The following day Peter went to the church, which was half a mile from their home. Mary stayed with the bodies of the children. In the church, he saw the old priest. After greeting him; Peter informed him of the heartfelt story. A neighborhood priest comforted Peter, praying for them. "They all must be buried in one united grave. This is one family," said Peter.

They both stood and went to the rectory. There, the priest gave a pick and shovel to Peter and said, "This is a tragic duty. I am very sorry; I do not have anyone appropriate to help you. The organist escaped, and I am too old." There is a small common cemetery behind the rectory. "There, you may dig," said the priest and pointed with his hand. This is a sacred place near the high golden cross.

February 3, 1945. Snow and frost crept outside. Peter was digging shallow multiple graves for three hours in the frozen earth. When Peter had finished his task, it was almost noon. A priest lent Peter a special wagon to transport the children's torn bodies. Peter silently pulled the wagon home. One of the neighbors in the street recognized him, and said, "What happened Peter?"

"The grenades killed my children, and my friend. I'm going to prepare their bodies, to deliver them to God and the cemetery," said Peter.

"I'm truly sorry about that. It's a great loss for your family," said the neighbor. "Let me come right now…to your home, and help you bring the little ones."

When Peter entered the house, Mary was waiting for him. Mary was wearing her prized coat. Frank, a neighbor, entered the home. He greeted Mary and said, "I am very sorry for what has happened. Let God, have them, in his hands." Peter and Frank gently wrapped John and Vladek in blankets

Peter and Frank laid their bodies on the cart which they pushed towards the cemetery. Several neighbors came out, reverently; to meet them. They walked in solemnity, where two neighbors consoled Mary, the crying Mother. Mary believed that she with many others would have to sacrifice in this difficult time. Mary said, "My children died innocently."

The shattered family came to the cemetery. The priest was waiting for them. In the distance, a patrol of Russian soldiers, curious, stopped to see a small solitary gathering, a funeral. When the patrol saw the bodies on the cart, the soldiers drove off looking at the family like they were victims.

John, Vladek and Hans were buried in one united grave. The priest said a few words. Peter, Frank and another consoling neighbor covered the bodies with icy frozen earth. Later he gave a small cross to Peter, who put it in the fresh soil. Mary could not leave the grave. Standing in stillness for a long time she cried, unable to reconcile events in her mind with the loss of her children. Peter thanked the neighbors for their help and heartfelt compassion. He lifted Mary by the arm and led her home. This hurt her the most. She blamed herself.

Fear reigned in the city. Russian occupational soldiers, plundered where they could. Citizens were terrified to go out into the street. They avoided having contact with the Russian army.

Charles arrived on a bicycle. He came to find out what the turmoil was with Peter and Mary. When he learned of the death of their children Charles sat down, collapsing in a chair. He convulsed like a baby. He could not believe what happened. Charles took some time before he came back to reality. He was with the neighbors and family for a while and left them two loaves of bread, a gift which he brought with him. He informed Peter that the owner of the bakery had work for him to do, because one of the workers was killed during the city's bombing.

Chapter XVI
Time After the War

L IFE WAS RETURNING IN FULL VIGOR. Slowly, daily a routine commenced with control over the city; where Peter lived with his family. Peter worked in a bakery together with his friend, Charles. Mary was again, at home and had great difficulty recovering from the loss of her children. She was often despondent. Winter and spring passed and on May 6, 1945; the Germans capitulated. The war ended relinquishing their territorial boundaries. There was great joy in Torun, and around the world. Poland was now free! This was a serious matter, in the minds of the people. Poland was under a new occupation, the Russians. In Poland, new communist authorities arrested sympathizers. Many were tortured and falsely condemned by the interrogation trials. Many more deaths followed, with suspected collaborators of the new pre-war liberation of the Polish government in England. Fear seized the people; a paralysis of apathy swept the atmosphere of delusion.

Peter put the house in order. In July 1945, Mary became pregnant. It was difficult to live, in these turbulent times. Many poles were missing many basic necessities of civilian life. Whoever had his sanity, had everything. The lack of trade and income dominated the working person's affairs of daily life. In the turmoil of events, Peter and Mary had forgotten about the mystery of

Andrews's treasure. One evening sitting at the table, Peter remembered the quiet and deliberate secrecy he had witnessed from Andrew. The following day, they both went to the cemetery. They searched the soil and debris around Andrew's parent's grave. Peter examined the tombstones. He found the place mentioned by Andrew where the hidden valuables resided.

The back of the monument revealed that it had a bottom made of plaster which was slightly brighter. "There is nothing I can do today. I will need a hammer and chisel. We'll return tomorrow," said Peter. The next day, after work, Peter and Mary arrived at the cemetery. In the distance, two people already were occupied cleaning tombstones. Peter looked around and crouched down. Mary was on the watch, cleaning the headstone. Peter wrapped his chisel with a cloth so that it would not make a sound. He began to hammer the plaster on the wall of the tombstone. After a few beatings, the plaster fell off and Peter carefully broke away four blocks from the back of the tombstone. There, exposed was a hole. Peter put his hand inside and pulled out a circular box six inches long with a diameter of four inches. Outside the box, was an empty space. Peter handed the box to Mary, who put it in the bag. Peter put the bricks in place and stood up. He looked around carefully and said, "Let's go slowly."

Outside on the road, Peter and Mary saw several police officers who were checking for necessary documents. They returned home and sighed a breath of relief. Peter placed the round box on the table and said to Mary, "Prepare tea." He then quickly covered the windows in the kitchen and locked the door.

Peter and Mary sat down at the table. "Open it up," said Mary. Peter tore off the tape, wrapped around the box. Then he unscrewed the bolts securing the lid and pulled on it. He turned the box upside down. Three Rusted bundles fell out on the table. Peter looked at the first bundle. Their eyes were surprised at what the bundles contained; ten small diamonds. The second bundle opened and contained six gold rings with a number of associated precious stones. Peter looked at the third bundle. He opened the cloth and saw twenty gold coins.

"This is a small fortune," said Peter. He then looked up to heaven and said, "Thank you, Andrew. You're a devoted friend. Mary, we cannot say a word about this to anyone, not even Charles. This will be our secret."

Life after the war was anxious. Peter had some stress because he was German. The new provincial government in Poland controlled by Russia was not liked by the people. The houses and land deeds were taken away from the pre-war gentry. The revised postwar Poland was said to have equality. Equality was only a forgotten idea. The security police were brutal and harsh. People lived from day to day in fear of breaking a rule.

In April of 1946, Mary gave birth to a 3rd son and named him Andrew. This was in remembrance of a friend who left them a fortune. Peter reached an agreement with the owner of the bakery Mr. Kozlowski and became its co-owner. He paid him with a handshake and two gold rings and two gold coins. Peter later enlarged the bakery and increased its production. To get anything accomplished; was to deliver a bribe. Peter bought land very inexpensively and cultivated grain and potatoes. The common sundry goods, that most sold in those days. Peter and Mary lived quiet decent lives; but often regretted the decision they made that evening, in Olsztyn. "What are Klaus and Horst doing now? What would happen to them?"

In June 1947, Mary gave birth to a daughter and gave her the name Margaret. Hannah, Adam and old Ted arrived at the party. They spoke frequently, about the past. Peter thanked them for their help in those difficult times. Peter was cautious of how they spent the inheritance money in order not to arouse suspicion. There were informers. The common people experienced unrest and turmoil because of them. Several times Mary and Peter helped their friend Charles. He wondered where Peter had hidden money. The money Charles received as a gift was a fortune. "You have been helping us in difficult times now, we are giving it back to you," said Peter.

In the year 1948, the postman brought a letter to Peter and Mary. They were told to report directly to the police station. They were frightened and had no idea what the letter was about. The following day, they both went to the police station. They stood before a policeman who asked, "Who do you know in America?"

Peter looked at the policemen and replied, "No one."

"Are you absolutely sure?" asked the policeman, cautiously.

Peter replied, "We have not been introduced to anyone," Peter answered again.

"Klaus Kremke. Does this name tell you anything?" Later, he impatiently threw the letter from America on the table. Here

Peter understood the intention of what the policemen were attempting to do. Peter had frustrated the policeman.

Peter said, "That is my cousin from the old Eastern Section of Prussia. I did not know that he relocated to America."

"We know that you were born in Germany. You now have a Polish wife and two children. A relevant history; you could be an enemy of Poland." Peter understood the seriousness of the accusations. He stood in silence. The impatient policeman looked at Peter and Mary diligently and ordered them to take the letter and go. When they were at the door, he added, "We will keep a close eye on both of you."

Returning later to the house, Mary grasped Peter under his arm, nervously. "They were alive. I'm happy," Mary said quietly.

When they came to the house, Peter looked at the envelope and said, "Someone has already read this letter. The letter was previously opened." He reopened the letter and began to read it aloud. It turned out, that Klaus lived with Gertrude and Horst in New York. Everyone was healthy. Klaus wrote this letter, not knowing whether anyone would live in this house. He asked about John and Vladek as well as about Hans. In the conclusion of his letter, he asked if Peter and his family would like to come to America. Peter understood the reason, to make a call to the police station. In this current season of time; the Security Office in Poland was controlled by the Russians. All outside foreign contacts were minimized and conversations were being monitored in strategically localized areas.

Peter and Mary thought all week of how to make an appropriate decision. They regretted that they did not go with

Horst. They regrettably missed a lot of opportunities. Living then in Poland was very primitive and difficult. They could not demonstrate the prosperity received from Andrew. They did not know, the extent of the fortune Horst left for them in the Swiss bank accounts. Peter and Mary were fearful to ask details of a national government bank. They did not trust the regular banking office. They finally decided most definitely, that there was a better life of opportunity in the west.

They decided, to write to Klaus and told him in reply they would be happy to immigrate to the United States; with heartache, Peter also wrote, what had happened to their children Vladek and John and old Hans. Peter continued writing about the children, Andrew, Margaret, Charles, and the bakery. In the adjoining letter, Mary attached a photograph of the whole family. Peter carried the letter to the post office, so that it could be sent to America.

Chapter XVII
Humiliation and Uncertainty

P ETER AND MARY WAITED IMPATIENTLY, for the answer of whether or not they would receive their passports. Unexpectedly, Peter received a notice that he was to appear in front of the commissioner at police headquarters, in a couple of days. Reading the notice, nervous apprehension appeared on the faces of Peter and Mary. "What do they want from you? Why are they only calling on you? I do not like this. You know, I have excellent intuitions," said Mary.

A week passed, and Peter went to the police station. Quickly, impatiently, the police verified his identity; Peter was then directed to the right person. Peter stood in front of a big brown door. On the door was a sign, Captain Murawski. Peter knew from experience that he didn't want to enter that door. He demonstrated minimal nervousness, to do so would be an obvious outward sign of weakness. "I must be strong," he said to himself. He breathed deeply, several times and knocked on the door, "Come in," Peter grasped the doorknob. When he entered the room, the police officer was sitting behind a desk on which lay a pile of papers.

"Peter Mayer?" The officer asked.

"Yes," Peter said confidently.

"Please, sit down," the policeman replied, firmly. Peter obeyed and sat down. The officer opened the file and began to read the document. After a moment he looked at Peter and asked, "Are you German?"

"Yes, I am," said Peter.

"Why did you stay here, and not make your way to Germany?" asked the officer.

"I have a wife who is Polish and I have two children. Why should I run away," Peter answered, trying to hide his increasing nervousness. The policeman stared coldly at Peter and asked, "What did you do during the war?" The question was a complete surprise for Peter. He did not know what to say. Would he answer him with the truth or with a lie?

In a fraction of a second a host of questions filtered through his head. "What do they know about me? If I tell the truth, will they surely believe me? If I lie, I will have bigger obstacles with more problems."

Peter answered and spoke about how he had to flee from his place of residence. He hid in the countryside, from the Germans until he was united with his family. "I'm not interested in how you ran away from the Germans. I would like to know what you did, during the war?" asked the policeman, firmly.

"I escaped with my wife and children to Olsztyn. That's where I worked cutting down trees."

"Whom did you live with?" asked the policeman,

"With my cousin," said Peter.

"What is their name and address?" the officer sternly asked.

Peter said, "Klaus Kremke"; and he also stated the address.

"Kremke? What happened next?" asked the officer?

"Later, I returned to my home and started working at the bakery," Peter replied.

"Are you a co-owner of the bakery?" asked the policeman.

"Yes, I am," said Peter.

"Where did you get the money to pay for the bakery?" asked the officer.

Peter could not tell the officer that he received the money from Andrew. "I traded before the war and earned a respectable amount of money. Business was accommodating," said Peter.

"Where did you get the vehicle?" asked the officer.

"The car belongs to the bakery," I was employed to bring bread to the surrounding shops. People need to eat," Peter replied.

The policeman looked at Peter and said, "That is all, for today. We must now take a closer look at you to see that you are not hostile to the Polish nation. All information regarding your testimony will be considered." Shivers went down Peter's back. "You can go now," the officer said. Peter stood up and left the police station.

Peter walked briskly on 'weak' legs. He reached the tram stop and sat on a bench waiting for his connection. Various thoughts came into his mind. The tram came to a stop. Peter boarded the tram and in 15 minutes he was home. When he entered the house, Mary sat, crying at the table. She threw herself on his neck, embracing him. She began to kiss his face with joy and happiness. Peter came home safe and sound. On many occasions, people were forced to endure increased interrogations and did not return home. They were arrested.

"How was it there? What did they want?" asked Mary.

"Give me a shot of vodka. I need a strong drink," said Peter. Mary quickly walked over to the cabinet and pulled out a bottle of vodka and two glasses. They both drank a shot of vodka. Peter took the bottle from Mary and sat down at the table. He had two more shots and drank them down, quickly. Peter gave Mary a brief description of the interrogation. "What will happen to us now? What do they want from you?" Mary asked, tentatively.

"I have to go to the bakery quickly and talk to Kozłowski." Without thinking, he stood up and left the house. The car was in the driveway and Peter drove away.

When Peter entered the bakery he walked straight to Kozlowski's office. "Hey, why are you so upset?" asked Kozlowski. Peter closed the door behind him and sat down on a chair in front of Kozlowski.

In a low voice, Peter asked, "Were the police here?"

Surprised, Kozłowski said, "No."

Peter breathed a sigh of relief, and said, "I was in the police station. They interrogated me and asked how I earned the money to purchase the bakery. I told the investigators that I had saved the money before the war. Fortunately, they did not ask me how much I gave to you. You must remember, I gave you the cash. We must all tell the same story."

"No problem," said Kozlowski. Peter finally calmed down. He then said that he must go home to speak with Mary, to have an early dinner.

Peter came home and talked to Mary; throughout the evening they discussed what to say, in the event of further hearings. They were both very upset. "We both have suffered so much, during the war. The communists are digging holes under us now. When it's over, it's over," said Mary. "Does this have anything to do with the invitation that we received from Klaus; for a trip to America?" They both wondered. They finally decided to wait, patiently for the continuation of events.

Two weeks passed. Peter stayed awake with Mary until four in the morning. Mary made coffee and breakfast. They both sat at the table drinking black coffee. Mary said, "Last night I had a bad dream. I dreamed that we were running away. I do not know what all this means. Peter, be careful." When Peter left the house, Mary went back to sleep.

Peter came to the bakery. He supervised the loading of bread crates and pallets within a second small van. Finally, around eight o'clock, Peter was tired and sat on a chair in the office. He then talked with Kozlowski about the current daily orders, and inventory for the bakery.

A police vehicle arrived in front of the bakery; two policemen stepped out of the car and entered the building. Peter and Kozlowski sat in the office when the door opened. The policeman entered the office. "Which one of you is Peter Mayer?"

"I am," Peter answered, and rose from his chair.

"You will please follow me, come to the station with us," said the policeman and escorted Peter to the car. The second policeman stayed with Kozlowski and asked him many questions; wanting insight into his relationship with Peter Mayer. After 10 minutes, the second policeman left the bakery and got into the waiting vehicle. Together with Peter, they both drove to the police station.

Peter was led within the station to a room where the same policeman had interrogated him earlier. He was already waiting for him. "Please, sit down," said the policeman. He looked at Peter and said, "Who are you? A spy? Who do you work for?"

Peter was very surprised, "I am not a spy."

The investigator looked at Peter and said, "You said, you lived in Olsztyn with your cousin, Klaus Kremke. We checked, your indicated address, nobody lived there during the war. Why did you lie?"

"I did not lie, I lived there," said Peter.

The policeman rose from behind the desk and stood behind Peter. "I'm going to ask you again, why did you lie?" Without waiting for an answer he hit him hard on the head. Peter fell from his chair to the floor from the force of the impact. "You're a spy! You obviously work in secret for the Germans!" the interrogator shouted. "You will eventually talk, and we will help you to change your mind."

The authorities were renowned for their brutality. Thousands of innocent people after the war were interrogated and tortured on mere suspicion. Most of them were sent to prison, tortured and died. The terror and intimidation on the part of the communists was unpredictable. It was the same with Peter. He was a German and the Polish authorities suspected every German of acting subversively against Poland. A number of holding and transit camps were established where Germans were also being held. Many were transported to work heavy labor within the mines where they were extracting coal. It was a hard and difficult time for people of German origin like Peter.

Peter, dazed, rose from the floor and sat down in his chair. He did not expect such violent and deliberate treatment from the hands of the police. Through his mind flew past, memories of interrogations by the Germans. Now, and again he found himself in the same situation with the Russian authorities. Instantly, Peter felt condemned by the entire situation, in which he found himself. He decided to say, what was agreed upon with Mary. The truth.

The lead investigator looked at Peter and said, "I have a lot of time. I am going to ask you again, what you were doing during the war." Peter understood the error he made. He had no choice but to tell the truth.

He breathed out, with emotion and said, "I told the truth. My cousin lived in Olsztyn, but then during that season, he was named Fisher. You can verify. He was involved in cutting down timber in the forests and trading in wood. I lived there with him, with my family. Later, I worked in a factory sewing clothes with various accessories. Then I came back here. When the front passed through the city, I lost two sons from the grenade explosions. Later I invested in a bakery. This is the whole truth."

The policeman looked at Peter and picked up the phone and said, "Put out a call for a Kowalski," then he put the phone down. After a while, Kowalski came in, and the interrogator said to Peter, "You're under arrest until we have the complete clarification of the case." To Kowalski, he said, "Take him into custody." Surprised and stunned, Peter lowered his head and was led out of the room by Kowalski.

Mary was preparing breakfast for her children when she saw Charles entering the yard. Her legs weakened under her. She knew something was wrong. After a moment, Charles came into the kitchen. Mary trembling asked, "What happened?"

Charles looked at Mary and in a low voice, he said, "Kozlowski sent me. The police arrested Peter. They came to the bakery for him. They also interrogated Kozłowski. What's going on here?"

Mary sat down on a chair with presumptions. "I had a bad dream last night. I knew something was going to go wrong. Two weeks ago, Peter was interrogated by the Russians. They asked what he was doing, during the war. He said that he lived in Olsztyn and worked for Klaus."

"But why did they interrogate him?" asked Charles. Mary looked at him and said. "Six months ago, we received a letter from Klaus; from America."

"What? He lives in the United States and you did not tell me the complete story," said Charles, who was surprised. "How are they doing?" he asked again.

"Life is good and marvelous for them. They live in New York. They have two sons," said Mary.

They both sat at the table. Mary said, "We did not want to say anything at that moment, Klaus asked in his letter if we would like to go to America. Three months later, we submitted all the relevant documents to the militia asking for permission to leave Poland. After two weeks, Peter was interrogated for the first time."

Charles embraced Mary and said, "Now, I understand your difficulty. The police verify every letter sent and received from abroad. You have to be selective and specific about what to say. Did Peter agree with you about what to say in case they interrogate you?"

"Yes," replied Mary.

"You have to say, the same thing. You cannot make common mistakes," said Charles. "Why didn't you trust me? I've been helping you all the time."

"Forgive us. We did not want to expose anyone. You know fully well; what kind of a time it is right now. You are our friend, forever. In addition to my sister, we have no one to depend on," said Mary.

Charles rose from the table and said, "I have to return to the bakery. Take care of your children. I will return here after work."

After work, Charles went home quickly and told his wife, Sophie about Peter's arrest. "Oh. No! They will abuse him again. Go and keep her encouraged," said Sophie. Charles left the house in a hurry and went directly to Mary.

Mary and Charles waited anxiously, until six o'clock in the evening. Finally, Mary decided to go to the police station and ask about Peter. "I will stay with your children," said Charles. Mary dressed in her coat putting it on nervously; she could not fasten all the buttons. Charles grabbed her hands and said, "Calm down, breathe deeply a few times." Mary obediently did what Charles told her. After a moment, she finished buttoning her coat and left the house.

Mary entered the Police building on her exhausted legs. She was nervous when she stood before the duty policeman. "How can I serve you?" asked the officer.

"My name is Mary Mayer. My husband Peter Mayer was arrested this morning. Peter has not come home. What has happened to him?" asked Mary.

The officer made a phone call and spoke into the phone, "Mary Mayer is here." After a moment, he put the phone down and said, "Please, sit down there in the chair and wait." Her legs weakened under her. She barely reached the chair. Mary knew something was very wrong. There were thousands of negative thoughts going through her head. They survived the turmoil during the war and now, the police wanted to further interrogate him. She did not understand, why.

After ten minutes, a young man came to Mary and asked, "Mary Mayer,"

"Yes," replied Mary.

"Please, follow me," The policeman led her in front of a large, heavy brown door. On the door the words were written, "Captain Murawski."

A young policeman knocked on the door. Behind the ominous door a voice was heard, "Come in." He opened the door and ordered Mary to come inside.

"Please, sit down," the police officer continued, saying, "How can I help you?"...; he was simply pretending, not to know, what was going on.

"You arrested my husband, Peter Mayer. He did not come home. What happened to him?" asked Mary.

"Oh. Peter Mayer? Yes... We arrested him. He gave false testimony two weeks ago," said the officer.

Mary had to be very shrewd regarding what she was going to say. She could not speak anything contrary to what she had first agreed, with Peter. "I do not understand," said Mary.

"Your husband testified that you lived in Olsztyn, with your cousin; and gave us the name Klaus Kremke. We verified and checked the name. The person he spoke of did not live there. He lied," said the policeman.

"It is impossible. He really lived there," said Mary.

"I see you are lying too," replied the policeman.

"Why would I lie? I'm telling the truth," said Mary.

"It will soon become clear; if you are telling the truth. Your husband is detained, to be questioned until the case is resolved. This conversation is now over," the officer said and ordered Mary to leave the room.

Mary, who was dazed and confused, returned home. Charles was waiting impatiently for her return. When Mary entered the kitchen, he knew something was wrong. "Where are my children?" Mary asked.

"I put them to sleep in the bedroom. They were tired of waiting for you." Charles waited impatiently until Mary sat at the table. Hot tea was prepared on the stove. Charles gave Mary a cup of tea and sat down in front of her. Mary was drinking the hot tea slowly.

Finally, she paused; and said, "They suspect that Peter deliberately lied concerning his spoken testimony. He said that we lived in Olsztyn with our cousin Klaus Kremke. They claim that he did not live there. I testified to it but the officer said that I was lying." There was a moment of silence.

Charles looked at Mary and said, "What was Klaus's given name before the war?"

"I don't know," Mary asked, dumbfounded.

"What was Klaus's name after the war? Was he not, named, Kremke?" asked Charles? Mary began to wonder.

Her eyes opened wide. She put her hands on her mouth and said in a low trembling voice, "Fisher. Klaus Fisher. Oh Jesus, what a mistake we made. What will happen now?" asked Mary; emotionally continuing, "What will he do now? This policeman said that Peter will be detained until they resolve this matter."

"Tomorrow, I will go to the station and tell the officer what Klaus' given name was, identified at birth. I have no idea if Peter remembered Klaus' given last name. You know, he had difficulty with memory." Mary uttered. Charles stayed with Mary and agreed that he would return, at nine o'clock to look after her children when Mary would go to the police headquarters. Charles then said goodbye to Mary and returned home.

In the morning, Charles came to the bakery and first spoke to Kozłowski about Peter. Regarding the conversation, Kozłowski said that he would be asking the police about Peter. "Load the bread into a truck and when you're done, drive to Mary." Charles dutifully obeyed the boss's order and returned to Mary at nine. Mary left Andrew and Margaret with Charles and went to the police municipal building.

At the police station, Mary said she wanted to speak with Captain Murawski. The policeman at the municipal building on duty made a telephone call. After a moment, he said, "Captain Murawski is waiting for you." Mary, with a beating heart, stood in front of Captain Murawski's door. She knocked slowly twice and heard, "Come in."

Mary hesitatingly entered the interrogation room and without waiting for the police officer's questions, Mary said, "Before the war, Klaus was named Fisher. If my husband informed you that Klaus was named Kremke, he was telling you the truth. When we saw him, he recently had documents for that given name. Will you release my husband?"

"Dear Madam, this is very serious. We have to verify details. You're intending to immigrate to America. Yes?" asked officer.

"Yes," said Mary.

"We have to notarize everything to protect our citizens. Especially when they are Germans," said Captain Murawski sarcastically.

"He is my husband," said Mary.

"Goodbye lady," said the Captain and ordered Mary to leave. Mary, overwhelmed and desperate left the commander's office and went home.

Days passed and Peter remained in custody. Peter was relentlessly questioned by the investigating municipal authority. After two weeks, tired, worn-out and bruised Peter sat in a chair in front of officer Murawski. "We retrieved information about your cousin, Klaus Kremke alias Fisher. He has a rich colorful past. He escaped the alternative, a bullet in the head for what he was ordered to do, in Stalag 18. You can now forget about going to America," said officer Murawski, smiling mockingly under his breath. He added, "You will tell us, what you know. We'll squeeze the last juices, out of you. You're obviously a spy." The policeman pushed the button and a large broad-shouldered man entered the room. He took Peter to his holding cell.

Earlier the previous day, sitting in the cell Peter was thinking about what he should do next. He survived the turmoil of the war and believed that the worst was behind him. He was wrong. The communists interrogated, relentlessly; primarily because of the letter and the desire of many immigrants to immigrate to America. He wondered if it was worth writing back. Various thoughts entered his mind. He finally, came to the conclusion that he must "come clean" or end up like many innocent people in prison or end up with a bullet in his head.

After three days, Peter was taken to the back, to a "special" interrogation room. There was a chair in the middle of the room. Peter knew what was waiting for him. He prayed, "God help me. I have to survive. I have a wife and children. I have to survive. I will survive."

Murawski was sitting at the table. After a moment of silence, he said, "Well, let's start from the beginning". Alongside Murawski was a large man with a strange smile on his face; he slowly approached Peter.

He leaned over to Peter and said, "This is for lying from the beginning," and punched him in the face. Peter began to answer every question that was asked of him. He delivered to Murawski the entire testimony of his war experience. The interrogation lasted approximately two hours. Tired and beaten Peter was returned to his holding cell, escorted by the guard.

For the next four days, Peter was repeatedly interrogated and spoke exactly the same as on the first day. His confession could not be wrong, because he would be tortured for pleasure. The police and the security office acted unlawfully, in Poland. They did what was unlawful and expedient with the prisoners. Peter was unjustly detained for two additional months.

Finally, one rainy morning, Peter heard from Murawski, "You're leaving, tomorrow. This time, you have earned your release; we have decided to be merciful." Great relief reigned in the heart of Peter. When he was alone in his assigned interrogation cell, he was overcome with sweet elation and great relief and began to cry with happiness.

Mary spent two additional months, waiting impatiently and praying for Peter. Neighbors helped Mary as much as they were able to. Charles reassured her, frequently. He brought bread from the bakery. Although Peter did not work in the bakery, Kozłowski fulfilled his obligation and gave Mary money from the proceeds. Thanks to the generous partnership with Peter, he developed the bakery as a business that earned a profit. The profit was more than he ever did by himself in the past. Kozłowski was very grateful to him for that. Andrew was older than Margaret. He began to speak. He continued to ask about father. Mary explained to him that he had traveled from a faraway place to work and would be back soon.

One afternoon, the black staff car parked in front of Mary's house. The policeman knocked on the door. Mary opened the door trembling. The visit of the militia was never a hopeful sign. Impatiently, the policeman said, "Tomorrow at 10 am, your husband comes out of custody. You will bring him clothes. He will be released". This message fell on Mary like a bolt of lightning from heaven. Mary began to cry tears of joy. The militiaman left and Mary was alone with the children.

After a moment, a neighbor went into the house and asked what happened. Mary replied ecstatically, "Peter will be released from jail tomorrow." The neighbor embraced Mary with joy and both cried with happiness. They knew that many people were in similar situations like Peter who never again saw the light of day.

They died being tortured, tormented and killed. The deliberate suspicion of the Polish authorities bordered on deliberate insanity.

Mary prepared clothes for Peter. Charles picked her up; they went to the militia station using the official vehicle given by Kozłowski. Mary entered the building at nine in the morning and handed the package to the officer on duty. The officer instructed her to sit on a chair in the hallway and wait. It was approaching ten in the morning, when a door in the corridor slowly opened, and she saw a man. He was gaunt with long oily hair and a beard. It was Peter. She threw herself on his neck and began to kiss him with relief and happiness. Both of them left the building and went to the car. Charles greeted Peter warmly. The family excitedly got into the car. Charles drove away from the station.

At home, Peter at the sight of his assembled children, Andrew and Margaret, rejoiced with delight. He squeezed them heartily and kissed them whenever he could. Faith and love for the family kept him spiritually alive in custody. He was home at last. The neighbors greeted Peter and said that he could count on their help. After a moment, Peter was alone with Mary and the children. They sat at the table. Mary slowly prepared a hot meal for Peter. He had not been privy to a hot meal for two months. After lunch, Mary poured hot water into the tub. Peter slowly lowered himself, sinking in the cast iron tub filled with warm water. He lay in the bathtub for a long time; Mary started washing his body. She noticed how his body was emaciated and bruised. He put on clean clothes and lay in a clean bed. He was embracing Andrew and Margaret together, and fell asleep.

A week passed before Peter resolved to forgive himself mentally and physically. He went to the bakery. He greeted friends and employees and sat down with Kozłowski in his office. They talked for an extended period of time and decided that everything would remain the same.

Several months passed. Andrew and Margaret grew up and Peter and Mary devoted the necessary time to them, and to each other. Peter could not be reconciled with the method of the Polish authorities in the way they treated him. He explained to himself, "I did not divulge state security secrets during the war. I fought only for my survival. And the fact that I'm of German origin has nothing to do with me personally. I have lost a lot but life must go on. I have a family, and I must take care of them." After a long conversation with Mary they decided, abruptly to escape from Poland and immigrate immediately to America. They knew the move was necessary and very dangerous. The consequences of a failed escape can be predictable. A long prison stay or a bullet to the head, not only for him but also for Mary. What about the children? This matter did not give him peace. Peter waited patiently and looked for every available opportunity and was very enterprising in that direction. He was looking for the best way out of the country.

Peter and Mary decided to speak directly to Charles about their decision. The conversation was specific and deliberate. They discussed various options. Poland was surrounded on all sides by communist countries. It was impossible to travel with the whole family, outside the borders of any country. Peter, with his past, would not have been able to get a permit to leave the country. There was nowhere to run. The only escape was the right passage through the Baltic Sea. But, how to do it? "I had a few friends in Gdansk before the war," said Peter. "I will have to go there."

"It's best that you all go there for vacation. Mary will take care of the children, you will have time to do your business," said Charles

"We have money," said Peter. "We'll pay the necessary, funds and tariffs as we need."

It was the beginning of June 1949. Peter with his whole family went by train on vacation to the Baltic Sea. The children enjoyed the beautiful sandy beach and bathed in the waves of the Baltic Sea. They had great fun. Mary did not take her eyes off of the children. She watched them as any good mother would.

Peter found two of his old friends. They talked about their wartime experiences. One of them, Bruno had a cousin who had a fishing boat. Peter was very cautious; he did not openly share his intentions. Bruno gave him the name and address of his cousin. "I would love to go there; I have never been to Ustka," said Peter. "My cousin is a good man. He also survived tumults during the war. Greet him from me and say, Mother greets him with a kiss, " said Bruno. Peter met twice with Bruno before saying goodbye and relocating to Ustka.

Chapter XVIII
A Spark of Hope

THE FAMILY CAME TO USTKA and rented a room approximately two blocks from the Baltic Sea. In the evening Peter went to the address given by his friend Bruno. He stood in front of a modest home. He knocked on the door. No one answered. He knocked again. Only silence. An old man came out from the neighboring house and asked, "Who are you and what do you want?"

"I am Peter and I'm looking for Andy. Bruno gave me his address," replied Peter.

"Andy is coming back tomorrow. He is fishing; Bruno is a good man," said the older man.

"Could you give him my address where I live? I'm here on vacation with my family," asked Peter. Peter gave the old man the address where he was staying.

"Okay. I'll tell him. I know where it is," said Andy's neighbor.

"Thank you," said Peter and then he said goodbye.

The following evening, a tall man entered a house where Peter rented a flat and asked for Peter. The owner of the house showed him a room at the back of the house. The man knocked on the door. Peter opened the door. The stranger said, "I'm looking for Peter."

Peter answered, "I am Peter."

"I'm Andy," said the stranger. "Nice to meet you, please come inside," said Peter. Andy walked into the room. Peter introduced him to Mary and the children. Everyone gathered at the table and began to talk. Peter said who he was and how he was employed. He gave greetings from Bruno, "Mother greets him with a kiss."

Andy understood the meaning of these words. These words were a signal that he could trust that person. Andy did not have a mother, she died before the war. Mary asked if Andy would like a drink. "Yes," replied Andy. Peter pulled out a bottle of vodka. He put the vodka on the table with three glasses. They talked and drank for a long time. They agreed that Andy would take Peter to catch fish at sea. Peter learned that Andy was lonely; his wife died before the end of the war. He lived modestly, alone in his efficient home. Andy spent most of his time at sea. It was a difficult job but he could earn a living from it. Fishing as a fisherman was all that he could do. He had his own fishing boat, which he inherited from his father. After the war, he renovated it and earned a decent living. It was late and Andy went home.

Two long uneventful days passed, Andy with Peter and two other fishermen arose at 5 am and sailed out to sea. They were fishing at the shoreline. They were careful not to go too far out to sea. It was not very fruitful fishing. In the afternoon they returned to port. Andy sold a small amount of fish in the fishery, a marketplace where they bought fish. He left a fish for Peter's family. The following two weeks, Peter made friends with Andy. He learned from him that he needed to repair the engine in the boat. For this, he needed more money, which Andy did not have. Andy did not know where to receive a loan. The bank did not want to give him a standard loan. The boat was worn and very old. Peter had to be secretive about what he was doing. Everything was carefully planned. Peter thought about every word with each drink of vodka.

The day before Peter's departure, he met Andy and asked, "How much will the engine cost?"

"A great deal of money, a few thousand. I would have to work a year, for that kind of money, at the factory," said Andy.

"Maybe I could help you," Peter said unexpectedly.

Andy looked at Peter and asked, "Would you really do that?"

"We'll speak again when I come alone in the next two weeks. Currently, I have to return home with my family. No one knows about our conversation," said Peter.

"You can trust me," Andy replied. They talked for a moment and said their goodbyes, arranging a specific date to meet again.

Peter and Mary along with their children returned after three weeks of vacation. On their way, Peter talked endlessly with Mary. "I need to think this through. I did not speak to Andy about anything yet. I have to be deliberate. I'll talk more with Charles when we arrive home. The most important facts are that you and the children had a vacation," and he kissed Mary on her forehead.

When Peter came home, he spoke to Charles. In their conversation, the plan was expounded. They were to board Andy's boat, sail to the Danish island of Bornholm, and seek asylum. Implementation of this plan was extremely difficult with the possibility of certain failure. Consequences were indeed, very serious. The only way out of this circumstance was to include Andy in Peter's plan.

"But can you trust him?" asked Charles.

"That's the thousand dollar question," said Peter. Peter thought about this for a while. It was time to travel to Ustka. Peter told Kozłowski that he must first go to Gdansk.

"Why are you going there? You were just there," asked Kozłowski.

"I want to invest in a small shop by the sea," said Peter. Peter did not reveal to Kozłowski that he was in Ustka for his own safety. The following day, early in the morning, Peter said his goodbyes to Mary and boarded the train.

Peter arrived, in the evening, at Andy's home. They talked about many current events, for a long time. Peter learned that Andy did not like the political climate in Poland. It was later determined that Andy could not make a large sum of money with a small boat. It's more than just survival in a very difficult situation that he found himself in. "That's why I'm here," said Peter. Peter put all his cards on the table "Do you want to make a significant amount of money?" asked Peter.

Andy looked at Peter and said, "Everyone would like to do this; but just what do you mean?"

"Do you want to leave Poland," asked Peter. Andy's eyes widened. He was speechless. Peter did not know what to say.

"Are you serious?" asked Andy.

"Yes, I'm serious," answered Peter looking directly into Andy's eyes. Peter studied his behavior.

Andy played his final card and said, "Would you like to escape with my fishing boat, going west?"

"Yes," said Peter in a firm voice. Andy leaped up from the table and went to the window and closed it, covering it with a curtain.

Andy checked the door and went to the cabinet and pulled out a bottle of whiskey and set it on the table. He poured whiskey into both their glasses and said, "I have no vodka. I kept this for a very special occasion. Let's drink and have a toast."

Peter and Andy drank the contents of their glasses expeditiously in one gulp. "Now we can talk. I've been waiting for a perfect opportunity like this for a long time. I thought about this occasion frequently but I did not know how to repair the engine in my boat," said Andy.

"Now there are two of us. I have money to repair the engine," said Peter. At the end of their conversation, Peter said that if everything goes well, Andy could flee with them to America.

Andy listened carefully to what Peter was saying. He thought for a moment about this and said, "A tempting suggestion but difficult to implement. Border patrols control the Polish territorial waters of the Baltic Sea. For this, you need specific times and carefully coordinated preparation. I've heard about a few cases of success. Many of the runaways, who have been caught, have finished their life in jail or have been shot. Secondly, my boat needs an overhauled engine. If you're discussing the costs of just such an intention, it must be a very powerful engine with the necessary speed for an escape."

"How much money do you need?" asked Peter.

Andy said, "10,000 zlotys."

"No problem," replied Peter, and continued, "Unfortunately, I cannot come here again. My partner may suspect something. I have to be cautious. First, tell me, do you agree to escape?"

Andy stared intently at Peter and said, "Here, in this land of occupation, I will not get rich. Will you help me later?" asked Andy.

"I give you my word," answered Peter. At these words, Andy reached out his hand, for the agreement. Peter was prepared for this moment and pulled a roll of money out of his pocket. He unfolded the currency and counted 10,000 zlotys. He put it on the table. Peter then added, "That's for your current expenses." Peter gave Andy an additional 1,000 zlotys. Andy had never seen all that money at once. It was a small fortune. Many hard working men would have to work two years or more to earn this sum. The two men sat for a long time talking about the details of the escape, sipping whiskey.

Early in the morning, Peter left Andy and went home. Later at sunset in the evening of the same day, Peter was at his home. Mary was impatient when Peter was away. She said, "Kozłowski came to visit me yesterday and he asked about you. I did not reveal anything except that you went to Gdansk to do business. He was not happy about that."

"Why did he ask you? I told him that I was going to Gdansk. We must be careful," said Peter. Sitting at the table he spoke to Mary about his conversation with Andy.

"Do you remember my dream, specifically of the arrest, and that we were running away? I'm scared but I'm strangely calm," said Mary.

"That's a good sign. You must always have hope and the anticipation of change," said Peter and then he added, "Let's go to bed, it's late." The couple then fell asleep.

The following day, Peter arrived at work. A customary greeting and then Kozłowski asked him, "How was Gdansk?"

"The owner wants too much money for a store. I told the owner, I had to consult my wife," said Peter.

"What's the business?" asked Kozłowski.

"At the moment, I do not want to reveal this. Everything in its time" replied Peter. Late in the afternoon, Charles and Sophie came to see Peter and Mary. After a long conversation, Peter and Charles went into the garden. Peter told him of his conversation with Andy.

After a moment, Charles said, "You must be very tactful. Kozłowski inquired about you and acted like it was by chance. I do not like his behavior. You ha ave to prepare critical events with a timetable and important details. You can be calm about me. Sophie did not know anything."

"That's good. Let it stay that way," said Peter who added, "In two weeks I have to see Andy again. On this occasion I will not let Kozłowski know." When it was getting dark, Charles and Sophi went home.

Two weeks passed and Peter was preparing to leave to Ustka. Earlier, he told Kozłowski that he was going with his family to the village where Mary's sister lived. Sunrise Saturday morning, Peter brought Mary and their children to the bus station. Mary with her children would have the opportunity to go to her sister Hanna. Peter then ran to the railway station, which was 100 yards from the bus station. When Peter was entering the railway station, Kozłowski was passing nearby, bringing bread to several stores in the area.

It was then that Kozlowski noticed that Peter entered the building. "What was he doing there now?" he thought. "You can travel by bus to the village, not by train." Kozlowski quickly parked the small truck and went into the train station. He looked around and in the distance observed Peter who walked over to the platform. Peter waited and then boarded the train. "Where is the train going?" Kozlowski asked the railway man. The railway man was standing on the platform, he replied, "To Gdansk." Kozłowski wanted to verify where Peter would get off the train. The train departed from the station. "What is he plotting?" thought Kozłowski. He returned to the truck and drove away to deliver the rest of the bread to the other surrounding stores.

Peter arrived in Ustka late in the afternoon. Without wasting time Andy and Peter traveled to a small harbor on the river where Andy moored his fishing boat. Along the way, Andy told Peter about what he learned and observed. "The engine will be here in two weeks. Until then, I will know a lot more about what's going on. I looked and observed everything," said Andy.

"This time you must come to me. I have a partner, who is very suspicious," said Peter.

"No problem," said Andy. The two walked and after twenty minutes they were there.

"How do you escape from the coast guard? They are everywhere," asked Peter.

"Yes, this is the most difficult obstacle. When I come to you, I will have better news. I have a friend who works at the port authority board. He likes to drink. He talks too much when he is drinking. I can learn more from him," said Andy.

"Be deliberate and watchful," said Peter.

"Believe me, I am. I'm putting my head under the ax," stated Andy. In the evening, they returned home. For a long time, they were talking about the details of the escape. Finally, they went to bed. Early in the morning on Sunday, Peter boarded the train for home.

In the evening, Peter waited for Mary and the children at the bus station. It was eight in the evening when Mary stepped off the bus with Andrew and little Margaret. Together the family returned home. When the children went to sleep, Peter and Mary sat on the couch and talked at length about the future situation in which they found themselves.

The morning came and Peter went to the bakery. As usual, he did his job. During the routine at lunch, Kozlowski said to Peter, "How was it there in the village?"

"Well, the children had an adventure at the beach. We returned home late in the evening," said Peter.

"I'm delighted that you had a good time," Kozlowski replied to this knowing, that Peter was lying. "What's he up to?" wondered Kozlowski.

Peter wondered what to do with the home and with the bakery. He thought about selling the house and his shares in the bakery with the pretense that he is going to Gdansk or leave everything behind. The fortune that Peter received from Andrew was in emeralds, diamonds, and 4 gold coins. It was a fortune in Poland. Besides that, he had frugally saved currency in a Swiss bank, which he saved from Hans. He did not know the value of the fortune. Hans did not manage to tell him. In communist Poland, Peter could not accept or understand the advantage of it all. You couldn't trust the communists. He could not legally go abroad with his past. Therefore, after much consideration with Mary, they made a very abrupt and dangerous decision, "Runaway."

At the appointed time, Andy surprised Peter with a visit at his home. Charles was privy to everything. For his safety, Peter did not invite him to meet Andy. Peter, Mary, and Andy conversed for a considerable time about the details of the escape. Andy learned by observing the patrols, and went to see when the changes of their assigned schedules occurred. The information about ships sailing from Ustka was certainly very important. Andy intended to stay with Peter for three days.

The following day, Peter invited Andy to the downtown area. They visited this historic, ancient city. During the visit, Peter noticed Kozłowski on the other side of the street. He did not want Kozłowski to see him with Andy. "Let's go into the tavern for a glass of vodka," said Peter. He then opened the door to the pub.

Kozłowski, however; had been keeping an eye on him and noticed Peter's quick maneuver. Asking himself, "Why is he hiding from me? I know something is going on, but what?" thought Kozłowski.

After half an hour, Peter and Andy left the pub and walked towards the tram stop to arrive home not aware that they were being watched by Kozłowski. Once at home, when everyone went to sleep, Peter and Andy were considering the danger of the escape. The agreed plan was to leave the territorial waters of Poland which seemed difficult to implement. They would use the opportunity of the changing of the patrol on the border waters. The difficult portion of the mission would be to board Peter's family on the fishing boat. Andy stated that he would have the engine in one or two weeks. It will be a used refurbished engine that is steady but very powerful and give them high speed. Summer had just begun. The plan must be scrutinized. Finally, they both went to sleep. In the morning, Andy said goodbye to Mary. Peter drove Andy to the train station and then he went to the bakery, to work.

It was the end of, July 1949. Peter informed Kozłowski that he was taking Mary and the children to the village for three days. "Oh, so you're going to the countryside, with your family again?" Kozłowski asked.

"Yes. Children love the excitement there. I will also rest, after these long stressful days," said Peter.

On Saturday morning, Peter left the house with his family and went to the tram stop to take a tram to the bus station. On the tram, Peter noticed a man standing reading a newspaper. After 15 minutes the tram stopped at the station. Peter lifted a sleepy Margaret within his left hand and in the other hand he held a small suitcase and disembarked out of the streetcar. Mary held Andrew's hand and did the same. Peter bought tickets and anxiously waited for the bus. They had 30 minutes to leave. Peter went to the kiosk, to purchase something to drink. Passing the ticket office, he casually noticed the same stranger, a familiar man standing, next to the tram. Peter did not pay attention to this at the moment.

The bus finally arrived. Peter and his family boarded the bus and sat in the front. Slowly, the bus was filled with passengers. Just before the departure of the bus, a strange unidentified man boarded the bus. The stranger sat down near the rear of the bus. "Is it a coincidence?" Peter thought. After an hour of driving, the bus stopped at the layover of a small town.

Peter exited with his family along with several other passengers. Unexpectedly, the stranger also got out. Peter and Mary and the children walked to a wagon and greeted the coachman. It was Adam, Hanna's husband, Mary's sister. Mary with the children sat close. The family sat on the wagon and Peter chose to sit next to Adam. When they were ready, the horses started to move. Peter then turned, looking behind as if talking to Mary and then he furtively glanced back. The stranger was standing next to the kiosk. Peter told Adam to hurry the departure. The horses moved faster and disappeared around the corner. Peter turned back to converse with Mary. In the distance, he noticed a man running from behind the corner. The strange man slowed his running and watched the wagon drive away. Peter said nothing to Mary. He recognized him. This was the one who he listened to and was tortured in the police station. Then he thought, "Why I am being followed? I do not like any of this."

After three days, Peter appeared at the bakery, Kozłowski then said to Peter, "How was it in the village?"

"Good. Just too much vodka," said Peter and they both laughed. It was agreed that Peter would take the car today, and deliver the bread.

"I have some important tasks to do outside the city," said Kozłowski.

Peter continued, "No problem. I will be ready in approximately half an hour."

After loading all the bread crates, Peter began to deliver the bread. At the end of his route was the task of bringing bread to downtown stores. The routine always included purchases, within the route. It was almost 10 am when Peter was passing by police precinct headquarters.

He was traveling slowly; there was heavy traffic. In the distance, he saw Kozłowski entering the police prescient building.

"What was he doing there?" Peter drove past the police station and parked on an adjacent street. He got out of the car and went to the corner of the building where he bought a newspaper and then pretended to read it. Peter surveying the layout of the building. Kozłowski left the building in the company of an officer. They briefly spoke to each other and shook hands. A policeman was walking towards Peter. Peter recognized him. That was officer Murawski. Peter quickly returned to his car; beginning to think about this intently, "It's not possible. Could Kozłowski report me to the police? No, not to worry it's just a coincidence," Peter tried to explain this to himself. "I have to keep the situation in confidence to myself; I cannot worry Mary unnecessarily."

In the afternoon, Kozłowski appeared at the bakery. Peter asked, "Did you make an effort to settle affairs outside the city?"

"Yes," replied Kozłowski. "This required time and effort, but I have arranged everything. What about your business in Gdansk?" Kozłowski said, unexpectedly.

"I plan to invest in a restaurant in Gdansk. In a week I will go there, again," said Peter.

"Are you moving there?" asked Kozłowski.

"No. This is just a long-term investment," Peter replied. Peter now realized something was wrong. Kozłowski was plotting something; but what?

It was now time to leave. Peter related to Kozłowski that he was going to Gdansk, Saturday at 7 am in the morning. He would then return, perhaps ideally on Monday. "Departure day was no problem," said Kozłowski. This is certainly strange, thought Peter. Kozlowski always complained that there was more than enough work in the bakery, especially today. He stated that additional work was no problem.

In the morning Peter arrived at the railway station. He immediately purchased a train ticket to Gdansk. While waiting for the train; he walked on the platform. A man in a weathered straw hat came out of the building. Peter recognized this person. That was the same man who followed him on the tram and bus the previous day. The train arrived after 15 minutes and stopped at the platform. Peter boarded the train and looked for a free seat in the second-class compartment. Peter sat by the door. The ride in the coach was to last three hours. Peter settled into the compartment's corner. He put his hat over his eyes and pretended to be asleep.

Observing from under his hat, Peter watched the corridor. The minutes slowly passed. Peter noticed a man opening the door to the next compartment. The stranger did not enter it. The man opened the door of the compartment where Peter was sitting. Peter was to be, "asleep". The agent looked around the compartment as if he was searching for free space and noticed Peter. He withdrew discreetly and closed the door. Peter then fell into a sound sleep. He was awakened by the voice of the conductor, "We are approaching the destination, Gdansk." Peter gathered himself, stretched and went into the corridor; at the end of the corridor, Peter noticed an unidentified agent. Peter made it seem like he did not see him.

Ten minutes passed. The train stopped at the station in Gdansk. Peter exited the coach compartment of the train and headed towards the center of the city. On the way, he bought another newspaper at the newsstand. Peter glanced discreetly, back and saw the agent walking, at a safe distance. "I'm being followed. I have to lose him, in twenty minutes I have a train to catch to Ustka," resolved Peter. Peter then went on, and turned left into the first available street and began to run quickly. He saw the open gate into the operating building, entered into the doorway, and hid behind the door. Peter heard another pursuing man who halted in front of the open gate of the tenement house. The agent looked into the gate but did not notice anyone.

Peter standing behind the door heard "Where could he have gone?" The agent was not aware that Peter was hidden behind the door. Peter heard retreating footsteps.

In the courtyard between the buildings; Peter noticed, an elderly man. He went to him and asked, "Is there another way out from this area?" The stranger looked at him with complete surprise. Peter pulled 20 zlotys from his pocket and put money in the hand of the stranger.

The man looked at the currency and said, "Come with me." The man led Peter to the back of a nearby building. He opened a small door. "You will be safe going through there," said the old man.

"Thank you," Peter said as he walked onto a small street dividing the buildings. He looked around and walked quickly toward the train station. He purchased a ticket and waited for the train to Ustka.

To Peter's great relief, the train arrived on time. After five minutes, the train moved and Peter was on the way to Ustka. He breathed a sigh of relief. At last, he was safe but for how long?

The situation was becoming very dangerous. "How long, have they been watching me? What do they know about me?" Peter wondered.

The agent was walking on the street cursing under his breath; he believed that he was being made a fool. "Which tenement house did he enter?" he asked. "Or maybe he ran away? That's not possible. After all; I was discreetly careful," the agent explained to himself.

After a while, Peter reached his destination, Ustka. He decided not to tell Andy what had happened to him. Peter was concerned that Andy would withdraw his plans to escape. Peter put everything on "the table," talking to Andy, he asked about the details. Peter responded, "When can we escape?"

"Before I will answer listen to my plan," said Andy. "The coast guard boat leaves the port and patrols twice a day. The best time for us is in the early evening. Every voyage to the sea is reported to the port authority office. My boat is smaller than a standard fishing vessel. I don't have to moor in the vicinity where all the other fishing boats are. Fishermen know that I employ two crewmen who assist me in fishing. You will have to change your identity into one of them, and possibly grow a beard. One of the crewmen looks like you. It is a great risk, but everything is possible by God's providence. He will be with us. In front of the hull, I will build a small hiding place for your wife and children. We will sail to the sea in the evening, immediately after the patrol boat leaves. The patrols always exit on their route to the West and then travel to the East. We will go after them. The moment they turn to the East and disappear from our eyes, we will follow at full speed; to the northwest, towards Bornholm. In the afternoon, periodically there are cargo ships from Sweden or Norway who sail to the sea. We will follow them closely".

Peter asked, "And if by chance, we do not meet such a ship?"

Andy replied, "We will continue sailing, without their protection. We will then, assuredly encounter Polish fishing boats that will be fishing nearby. We must avoid them, and this will not be easy. The most important part of the plan is sailing out of the Polish zone, and this is 12 nautical miles. This is absolute madness! Must we risk our lives for the outcome? So think again, do you want to do it?" There was now only a momentary silence.

Peter looked at Andy and said, "I went through turmoil during the war. I lost two children. I have currency that I cannot use. What value is that to human life? What kind of future do I have in this country? We all know what we risk. We have decided to run away without a doubt." Peter did not mention that he was being followed for fear that Andy would withdraw his plan.

"I will need ten days to put the engine into the boat, and test it. Meanwhile; I will build a small hiding place for your family and gather additional fuel. When I'm ready for departure, I'll send you a greeting card or postcard from Gdansk," Andy said.

"Do not send the postcard to my address. Send the greeting card to Charles. It will be safer that way. We never know what will await us," said Peter.

"If you receive a greeting card from me, you will not have more than 10 days to arrive," Andy said. They both talked for a long time about the details before they fell asleep.

Early in the morning, Peter then said goodbye to Andy. He traveled back home. In Gdansk, Peter was watching at the railway station. He stood near the platform office and at the last moment, he boarded the train. Peter came home late in the evening. Tired, lying in his bed, he told Mary of the full account. "What are we going to do now?" Mary asked quietly.

"Sleep, everything will be all right," and they both fell asleep, peacefully.

The following day, Peter appeared in the bakery. Kozłowski immediately asked, "How was your trip to Gdansk?"

"Not bad. Slowly, this investment is taking time. This is not an easy decision. I will have to travel there with Mary to make the final arrangements," said Peter.

"Are you moving there? What will you do with the bakery?" asked Kozłowski.

"I do not know, yet," Peter answered. Peter did his regular assigned job at the bakery. He stealthily whispered to Charles, "After work, at the Barrel." Charles knew exactly what that meant, something was up and it required a mysterious, rendezvous at the Pub.

Peter and Charles met at the Barrel pub. They ordered herring and a bottle of vodka. Peter spoke in a quiet voice of his observations about Kozlowski. "That scoundrel," said Charles.

"You will receive a greeting card from Gdansk in approximately two weeks. Keep me informed, let me know of the details. This will be a sign to leave," said Peter. They both ate a snack and drank vodka.

At the end of the conversation, Peter explained to Charles that he was being followed. "Do you really want all this danger and turmoil?" asked Charles.

"I have no choice," replied Peter.

Charles then said, "Be careful." Then they both went home.

Kozłowski entered Captain Murawski's office. "Hello, Kozlowski," said Murawski. "I'm telling you that Mayer's is hiding information. He continues talking about some business in Gdansk but I do not believe him. You promised me that you will finish him."

"Don't worry. You will have your entire share in the bakery," said Murawski.

"Have you got the money? Fulfill this contract. Remember, you promised me the full delivery of bread to the military attaché and that's a lot of money for both of us. Time is running out and you must capitalize on this opportunity quickly," said Kozłowski.

"I will need two additional weeks. He will be in jail for a long time," said Murawski. Together with Kozłowski, they left the room.

Approaching the end of the week, Kozłowski walked back and forth pacing, nervously upset. Passing by Peter, he then asked, "When are you leaving to go to Gdansk?"

Peter, surprised by this question replied, "Why are you asking?"

"I'm just asking," said Kozlowski.

"I do not know yet. Maybe, I will know in a week or two."

"I need to know what to do," replied Kozłowski.

"You will learn about everything in time. I'm not positive yet if I will leave," said Peter. Kozłowski impatiently walked away. "I do not like his behavior," said Peter to himself.

A week had passed. It was Monday, as Peter was leaving the bakery, he approached a man in civilian clothes who said, "Mr. Mayer follow me." The man pointed to a parked car on the street. Peter knew the profile of the man in the vehicle. He had already noticed him at police headquarters.

Peter was led into Murawski's office. Murawski said, "We meet again. You are an unruly citizen. We must watch over our citizenry in the country."

"I do not understand Captain," said Peter.

"You'll soon understand. What did you do in Gdansk?" asked Murawski.

"How do you know that I was in Gdansk?" asked Peter, who pretended to be surprised. Murawski noticed that he had made a mistake.

"We must know everything, Citizen Mayer!" exclaimed Murawski.

"I want to invest in a store and move there," said Peter.

"Where did you obtain the money? You need a great deal of currency for that," said Murawski.

"I will sell my share in the bakery. We're doing well; I can get a fair price for my share of the bakery. Kozłowski will buy my share," said Peter.

"I do not think so," said Murawski.

"How do you know?" asked Peter.

Murawski was confused seeing that he had made a mistake, once again. With a rough voice he asked, "The store you want to open, is it not another bakery? Do not think of me as a fool. I don't joke around. I proved it once to you before."

"I will get an inquiry of every store to see if an owner wants to sell his store," Peter said hypothetically.

Murawski well knew that Peter was not fully committed; he then said "From today, onward every trip outside the city must be reported to me. Do you understand?"

"Yes, sir," replied Peter.

"You are free to go," said Murawski. Peter came out of the registry of command headquarters, upset and went straight home.

Mary was at home preparing dinner and watching Andrew and Margaret. When Peter came in, she was surprised and asked, "Why so early?"

Peter sat down at the table and greeted the children, paused and then said, "Could I have some dinner?" Mary put a plate of soup on the table. Peter ate the soup. He then fed Andrew and Margaret. He made a spectacle about it. Mary poured him another bowl. Peter then hung up his clothes and went out with the children and Mary, to the garden.

The children played happily in the garden. Sitting under a tree on the ledge Peter informed Mary that he had been detained. "I know that Kozłowski has had his hand in this. He wants to get rid of me. He will do anything to own the entire bakery. I believe that he desires to frame me and get me arrested." Peter embraced Mary and said, "They have been following me."

"What!" exclaimed Mary, who was surprised.

"I did not tell you this, but every time we left the city; someone followed us. When I went to Andy, a man followed me. I lost him in Gdansk," said Peter.

"What will happen now?" asked Mary, who was distraught.

"As we agreed, we're running away. It's now, or never," said Peter.

Three weeks had passed. Peter waited for a message from Andy. Finally, on Wednesday Charles gave Peter a postcard. He read, "Greetings. Visit me on holiday," Peter said quietly to Charles, 'Come to us today for dinner. Do not say anything to Sophie."

"We will come," Charles briefly replied. Late afternoon Charles appeared with Sophie. Mary then made a special dinner. She made roasted turkey and ham.

"What is the special occasion?" asked Sophie.

"We just wanted to have dinner with you," said Mary knowing that it was their final farewell, to Charles and Sophie. They had lived together for an extended period, and were grateful.

Dinner was finished, Mary left with Sophie to relax in the garden, where they played with the children. Peter stayed with Charles at home. They both conversed through the evening. Peter said, "Unfortunately, that the time has come to say goodbye." Peter gave Charles two large boxes of the most valuable items Peter and Mary, had at home. In addition, Peter gave Charles two emeralds, diamonds, and two gold coins. "It's all for you. You were a good friend," said Peter.

"It's a fortune! Where did you get the diamonds and coins?" asked Charles, who was surprised.

"From Andrew," said Peter. They both embraced and tears flowed down their cheeks.

"What will you do, with the house and bakery?" asked Andy.

"I would like to give you all this fortune, to inherit, but I hesitate, I'm afraid to do this. Our enemies would destroy you," said Peter

"I understand," said Charles.

"Tomorrow, I must tell Captain Murawski that I am going to the countryside on a weekend holiday. When I leave, I will not return here. I cannot travel by train. They have their agents in all the obvious places. I will have to come up with a convincing cover story. I do not know if we'll see each other again." Peter said with sadness in his voice.

"I wish you God's speed on your journey," said Charles.

When it was time for departing, Mary was crying saying goodbye to Sophia and Charles. "Do not cry Mary, soon we'll see each other, again. We will be reunited," said Sophie convinced that she would see Mary and her children again. Peter offered to drive them home. When they arrived at their home, Sophia said goodbye to Peter and entered the house. Peter and Charles were waiting for this, brief occasion. They quickly brought out two large trunks and carried them to the shed.

"When we leave on Sunday, unpack them quickly and arrange them at home; as if they were yours. Tell Sophia to be absolutely silent. For you, it is a small fortune. I have more than enough. Goodbye, my good friend," Peter said quietly. Then they said farewell again and Peter went away.

Thursday as he delivered the bread, Peter stopped at police headquarters. He informed Captain Murawski that he was going to the village Branik, to visit Mary's sister. "Please report immediately on Monday, when you return," said Captain Murwaski.

"Yes sir," said Peter and left the command. Murawski was plotting all the time about how to arrest Peter Mayer. When Peter left, he said to himself, "I'm going to get him now. Finally, I realize the implication of the promise given to Kozlowski. Arrest Mayer. Kozlowski will then have the entire bakery and I will have 10 percent from the bakery's inherited sale to the military unit, which I richly deserve. I will be able to afford luxury." He already had a master plan, firmly fixed in his mind.

On Saturday, early in the morning, Peter and his family traveled by tram to get to the bus station. Peter then noticed a black car which drove slowly in the distance. Peter at the bus station purchased tickets for the entire family and boarded the bus. When the bus set off; the black car was driving behind the bus, keeping a measured distance. When the bus stopped in the small city of Branik, Peter and his family got off. They moved towards the rendezvous point where they would meet with Adam. Adam arrived with his wagon. The family quickly stepped into the wagon and went deep into the countryside. The same black car followed them in the distance on their journey to Adam's house. When Adam came home, they all went in. After verifying where the family was, the black car then drove away.

A black municipal police car pulled up near Peter's house. Two policemen got out of the car and walked to the side door that led out into the garden. Suspicion caused the policemen to open the door. When they were inside, they closed the door behind them. Directly from the office of Murawski, they were ordered by a warrant to search the building; the policemen searched the entire house. They were looking for items that would help Murawski arrest Peter. They found nothing specific. Peter was shrewd. He previously removed documents and papers from his home that could implicate him. Sergeant Burek did what was commanded by Captain Murawski. He had placed a leaflet, defaming the Polish nation in the closet, under the clothing of Peter. The accusation was supposed to be an excuse to arrest and accuse him for the act of spying. They also made a detailed search of the vehicle from the bakery. Peter's car was parked in the yard but they found nothing besides the common business license and papers, from the bakery. After a while of searching, they stopped their search and left.

Late in the evening, Peter left the village on the last available bus to reach his house. He approached the home from afar. Peter carefully watched to observe if anyone was watching from his home. Peter saw that the area was clear of any hidden surveillance. Peter went into his house and put necessary items in two suitcases. He stood in the kitchen, looked around again and said, "I'm going to miss you all." He left the house after placing the suitcases in the car and drove off.

Peter entered Adam's house at midnight. He put Andrew and Margaret, who were asleep, in his car and covered them with blankets. They said their goodbyes to Adam and Hanna. Mary said to Hanna that they were going to Gdansk for vacation. Separating, they did not want to compromise their security. Hanna gave them the food they needed for the journey. Peter and Mary drove off into the dark night. On the way, they both prayed, asking God for continued help, grace, and protection. This was their most difficult and perilous test, involving their lives. They knew very well what dangers awaited them …freedom, imprisonment on their journey, or perhaps death.

Chapter XIX
Escape to Freedom

PETER AND HIS FAMILY ARRIVED IN Ustka, early in the morning. It was Sunday the final day of August. People assembled at church for the service and mass. Peter and his family went to the church to intercede and pray for the success of the escape. It was 9 o'clock in the morning when Peter took Mary and the children to the beach. He said, "Wait here until I return. I'm going to Andy." Peter then disappeared from Mary's sight.

Fortunately, Andy was at home together with his dog Roxy. He said, "I knew you would come today. Where is Mary and the children?"

"They're at the beach. I came directly by car from the bakery. Where should I leave it?" asked Peter.

"You will drive the vehicle into my shed. It will then be hidden and not be obvious. Nobody will find it there," Andy replied. They left the house and went to the beach.

Andy greeted Mary and the children. Andrew and Margaret had a relaxing day playing in the sand and water. A steady stream of vacationers came to the beach. Andy seeing Mary's apprehension said, "Now we're going to hide the car. We'll be back soon. Everything will be fine." Andy and Peter left the beach. They got into the car and drove to a secluded place where his boat was moored. Andy's shed stood between the trees. Peter parked the car on the street. Andy looked around cautiously. He opened the wooden door.

Peter drove inside. "One less problem out of the way to the path of freedom," Peter thought. Together they went to the boat. Andy showed him a small locker. It too was almost invisible, hidden in plain sight integrated into the prow of the boat covered with debris, supplies, and nets. "You hid that well," said Peter.

"I tried my best," replied Andy. "I knew it couldn't be too obvious, I hid it in plain sight. Now let's go, and enjoy the beach."

Peter and Andy returned to the beach. On the way, Peter bought lemonade to give to Mary and the family. The children especially liked this drink. They sat in a clearing off the beaten path and Andy started telling Peter and Mary how everything was prepared. "The engine worked flawlessly. The boat now had high power and speed. Andy also had a supply of fuel that he bought on the black market. They would wait for the Border guard's leave from the port heading west. Then they would turn back and follow an easterly course. They would then sail out, leaving in the evening.

"I have to report every trip in my log to the registry of the port authority. I will say that I have to check the engine again before I leave for fishing. In the evening, when the last patrol of the day leaves the inlet harbor; we will sail to the great inlet, of the Baltic Sea. This will all occur when we see in the distance, the last patrol of the day surveying on their rounds; coming back heading east and disappearing into the black sea. The darkness will veil their eyes. We will, therefore, use surprise stealth, and all the engine power and take a course to Bornholm. It is about 74 nautical miles. The rest is out of our hands and into God's hands. The most important key issue is to leave the territorial waters of Poland. This is about 12 nautical miles. This will all be very tedious. Patrols are patrolling at sea, there are obstacles and dangers. When we reach the Bornholm we will demand political asylum," Andy finished. There was now only one speculation. They all looked at each other with languishing eyes, "You all know what will happen if we do not manage the escape?" asked Andy. There was a moment of silence.

Mary said, "It appears heavy in words, but there will be sorrows. What will happen to us then?"

"It's difficult to predict or persevere with all these events. If we decide to focus on the big risks; we must be then prepared for success. I'm asking you again, do you want to take these risks?" Andy asked.

Peter looked at Mary and the children playing on the beach and said, "Yes. We're all running away."

"I'm with you," said Andy and added, "Will you help me later?"

Here Peter spoke up and said, "We give you our assurance that we will take you to America. You will not have to worry about money; we will have more than enough."

Mary pleaded again, "Deliver us out of this country, safely."

"I'll do my best," said Andy and offered his hand to Peter and Mary.

"We do not have sufficient time. I drove the car from the bakery and Kozłowski will deliberately search for me. I will not report to Kozłowski tomorrow, and they will certainly look for me," said Peter.

"Two Norwegian ships are scheduled to leave our port in two days. Our hope is delivered with them. We will attempt to catch them and hide under their cover. Let the sea be calm," said Andy. The family stayed on the beach for two additional hours. Later in the afternoon, Andy said, "Peter you all are tired. Go home and prepare dinner." Mary called Andrew and Margaret and the family returned to Andy's house.

The children could not wait to see Andy's dog, Roxy. Roxy stays with Andy's neighbor during Andy's absence. They remembered him from the vacation they had spent there. After arriving at Andy's home, Mary prepared dinner. Peter and Andy discussed the whole situation. The children played with Roxy.

Monday passed with final preparations. Andy and Peter provided a supply of drinking water and food on the boat. Only one more night remained. The family had a restless night of sleep from anxiety and fear.

The next day, in the morning, Andy went to the port to report that in the afternoon he would be out to sea. He decided to check the engine. The workers at the port asked him if he was taking someone with him. "Yes. I will have a small crew. Possible Tom or Luke," said Andy. Tom and Luke were the fishermen working for Andy.

"It will be windy today, in the afternoon," said one of the workers.

Surprised by the news, Andy replied, "It's good to troubleshoot the engine so that it would be more dependable with regular conditions before I go fishing in the sea. I did not fish for two weeks, I need money." said Andy with some hesitation. Andy asked, "Is there someone else leaving today from the port?"

"Two Norwegian ships sail in the evening. I will observe them to be sure none of them will ram you," said one of Andy's colleagues.

"I'm not afraid, my boat is quicker than theirs," said Andy and everyone started laughing. Andy then said goodbye to them and returned home.

Peter and Mary waited impatiently for Andy's return. "Everything is prepared. Now we must be patient and wait," said Andy. Around noon the wind started blowing from the south. Four o'clock in the afternoon, zero hour; everyone was ready to leave. Andy retrieved the most important documents with him. He searched around the house and said his final "Goodbyes." Peter and his family left the house and headed towards the small inlet harbor, where Andy's boat was moored. Andy was the first to leave. Peter held Margaret in his arms. Mary was holding Roxy on a leash in one hand and Andrew's little hand in the other as they walked slowly to their destiny.

Finally, they reached the small inlet harbor obscured by camouflage debris and trees. Andy was already waiting for them. Peter handed Andy his children, first Andrew and then Margaret. Then Mary came on board and finally Peter holding Roxy. Andy and Peter looked around nervously to see if anyone was watching their preparations. They did not observe anyone. Andy ordered

Mary and the children to come down under the lower deck. They crawled to the very front where the hiding place was prepared for them. Little Margret started to cry because it was dark. "Do not be afraid I am with you," said Mary. Andrew embraced Roxy. Both were terrified because they were unaware of what was happening around them. Mary put her arms around the children and began to pray short prayers to God. Then Mary prayed longer prayers.

Kozłowski arrived late Sunday at the bakery. Four bakers worked extended shifts at the bakery. This time it was Kozlowski's night to work. He exchanged shifts with Peter every other week. Kozłowski knew that Peter was driving the bakery car. Peter always began his shift at work at five in the morning the following day. Monday morning at six o'clock Kozlowski asked Charles if he knew what was happening with Peter. "I have no idea. I have not seen him since Friday." Kozłowski waited impatiently for a Peter until eight o'clock. Peter did not show up for his scheduled shift at the bakery. He decided to drive to Peter's house. When he arrived there, he did not see the vehicle Peter drove. The doors were closed. He again pounded with anger at the door. It was empty and silent.

"I will get him," said Kozłowski with a slam. Kozlowski drove straight to the police headquarters.

Murawski was sitting in his office. The telephone rang. He answered the phone and listened. After a while, he said "Let him in," and hung up. Kozlowski entered into his office upset and said, "Mayer did not come in for his regular shift at work. I went by his home. The car was gone and the doors are closed. I knocked on the door and no one answered."

"He was instructed by protocol to report directly to me when he returned from the village," said Murawski. He picked up the phone and said, "Call Burek." After a moment Corporal Burek entered the room. Murawski said, "You will go directly to the house of Peter Mayer. Observe what is going on there. You know what to do."

"Yes, sir," said Burek as he left the room.

"Go to the bakery. If he appears there, you let me know immediately," said Murawski to Kozlovski. They both said goodbye to each other and Kozlowski left his office.

Sergeant Burek parked his vehicle outside Peter's house. He went to the door, knocked firmly and then said, "Open up, police." There was only silence. Then he pounded again, on the door and said, "Open up immediately, police. I will break down the door." There was no answer.

Standing next to Burek was a second officer, who asked, "You want me to kick down the door?"

"Yes," replied Burek and with his boot he kicked the door with rage, and all his strength. Burek stormed inside, with the second officer. The house was silent and empty. There was no one there. Burek was last there at the home on Saturday after the inspection during the absence of Peter and his family. Burek noticed that a few household items had disappeared from the house. He verified whether the leaflet he had put in under Peter's belongings was there. "It's there. Good," he said to himself. He then noticed a few suitcases missing. "We're going directly to Murawski," said Burek. They closed the door, got into their vehicle and drove off to the municipal headquarters.

Adam sat in front of his house when the police car pulled into his yard. Burek got out of the car and asked, "Where is Peter Mayer?"

"He is not here," said Adam. Hanna quickly saw the vehicle by the window and walked out from the house and stood by her husband Adam.

"Where is his wife and children?" asked Burek.

"They are not here. You can check to verify," replied Adam.

Hanna, frightened, asked her husband, "What is happening?"

"They're looking for Peter and Mary," said Adam. Burek entered the house without asking and they began checking all the rooms. The police turned over objects in the attic. There was no one.

"Check in the barn and the shed," said Burek to a second officer. "When did they leave?" asked Burek.

"Sunday night," replied Adam.

"Middle of the night?" asked Burek.

"Yes. By car," Adam answered.

The second officer came back and said, "The barn is empty."

"That bastard. He's' run away! No one gets away!" said Burek to his friend.

Adam embraced Hanna, who was frightened. She asked Burek, "What is this about?"

"You will find out later," said Burek, in a harsh tone, as he drove away with his friend.

It was three in the afternoon when sergeant Burek reported to Murawski and said, "They left Branik at 1 am. It looks like an escape was planned in advance. When we left him, he returned home in secret. He hastily gathered his things, the car, and then returned to the countryside. He came for his family and left. But where?"

"Those in the country?" asked Murawski.

"It seems that those in Branik do not know the details. We will press them for the truth," said Burek.

"How about his cousin at the bakery? Go and check," said Murawski. Burek then drove to the bakery.

In the bakery, Sergeant Burek met Kozłowski. "He's not here. He disappeared!" Kozłowski shouted in the distance.

"Where is Mayer's cousin? Bring him to me," said Burek. Kozlowski went into the bakery and soon appeared with Charles.

"Tell me, when was the last time you saw Peter Mayer?" asked Burek.

"Friday after work," replied Charles.

"Did he mention where they were going?" asked the policeman.

"He said he was going to the countryside with his family," replied Charles, pretending to be surprised.

"We'll talk to you later. You can leave," said Burek.

Charles left the room and said to himself, "They are already looking for him. God, help him to escape." Burek asked Kozlowski about the specific account related to the disappearance of Peter. Kozłowski related the same story that he spoke to Murawski, which Peter was leaving often to Gdansk as a particular matter of some interest. But he was always mysterious about it.

"If Mayer comes back, let us know immediately!" Burek told Kozłowski. Sergeant Burek left the room and drove off to the municipal police headquarters. Kozłowski then sat down comfortably in his chair, lit a cigarette and said to himself, "The bakery is already mine. I own it, and will profit from it in the future."

Burek reported to Murawski and spoke to him about his visit to the bakery. Murawski knew that Peter was a shrewd man and wondered. Where did he go? The trail ended at Gdansk. But was he there? So when he was fooling our agent, he had to go somewhere. But where? That was a complete mystery for Murawski. He stood upright on his feet and went directly to his supervisor Janikowski and presented him with all the information he had on Peter's disappearance.

"Notify headquarters in Gdańsk and the surrounding areas. Provide a description of the fleeing family with the vehicle registration number of the car. In the event of the detainee's arrest, they must follow protocol and notify us immediately," said Janikowski. Murawski left the office and went to deliver the direct order from the administration of police.

It was August 31, 1949, six in the evening. Andy was sailing along the port channel. On the way, he noticed his colleague Paul from the Port Administration office. He nodded to Andy, and then said goodbye and went on. He noticed another man on board. He had a beard and turned his back to him. "It's probably Luke," Paul reasoned as he entered the port office building. He had an additional two hours of shift work. Andy sailed out of the port onto the rolling sea in the most dangerous journey of his life. A journey of exploits peril to freedom.

On the port side of the boat, a patrol ship sailed in the closing distance. On the right side of the boat, Andy noticed a ship that sailed in a direct line in front of them. Half an hour before him sailed a third ship, which headed towards the island of Bornholm. Remaining in a safe distance from the shore, Andy allowed Mary to leave the compartment of the hiding place inside the boat. Mary sat down on a small bench in the cockpit's cabin. Margaret clung to Mary with fear. Peter embraced Andrew. The south wind was blowing briskly. Andy was sailing slowly. About an hour and a half after sailing into the sea, Andy noticed in his searchlight that the patrol boat was turning east. Now, you all have to remain hidden so that you can't be seen. They might search looking through binoculars. The boat passed them about two miles ahead. "We have to be patient," Andy told Peter. The horizon was clear on a cloudless night. In the distance, Andy could see the outline of stars and the cargo ship that sailed before them.

Thirty minutes later the patrol boat disappeared from sight. Andy's boat was about 4 miles out from the distant shore. Finally, Andy said, "In the name of God." Now, he pressed on the gas. The engine choked with black smoke and accelerated.

They moved with great speed. The small boat began to cut a wake on the waves held by the wind. They changed course northwest to Bornholm. Andy pressed onward; Mary went out with the children from the hiding place and sat with them in the hidden compartment next to Andy and Peter. It was getting dark. Andy decided to keep it dark with the light at the stern of the boat. He did not want to attract unnecessary attention but used surprise and stealth to work in his favor.

Paul completed work and went home. Along the way, he met a friend who invited him to stay for a glass of chilled vodka. They went to the pub. In the corner of the pub, he noticed Luke and Tom, Andy's workmen sitting at the table. He went to them and asked, "May we sit down?"

"Of course. Please, sit down," said Luke.

"Luke you returned from the sea," said Paul to Luke.

"What sea?" Luke asked very surprised.

"Do not deliver a long story. I saw you on a boat with Andy, approximately two hours ago, you were leaving port," Paul said.

"Man, we've been sitting here for three long hours drinking vodka with colleagues. We have not seen Andy for a week. He said that he had something to do in Gdansk. When he returns, we'll be sailing directly out to sea," said Luke.

"Andy was in the office today, and said that he would take one of you with him and operate an engine test," said Paul.

"The engine is operating. We tested it a few days ago," said Luke.

"Who was with Andy today on the boat? Something is not right here," said Paul. He rose from the table and left.

"What is he raving about?" asked Tom, who was drunk.

"I have no idea," answered Luke as he finished a tall glass of vodka with Paul's colleague.

Working in the port office, Paul was always very deliberate and professional. "Something is not right, here," he said to himself. Paul went back to the port office, but he did not see Andy returning from the sea. Paul understood what he was supposed to do at such a time. He went straight to the coast guard building. He was familiar with the staff in the facility. After his greeting, he spoke to the officer on duty and explained to him the entire situation. "It is dark and he should be back soon," Paul said.

"I believe that the situation is serious. Do you know where he lives," said the officer.

"Yes," Paul replied.

"Will you come with me," said the duty officer. They both left the building. At Andy's house, it was evening. The door was locked. "Do you know where he moored his boat?" asked the duty officer Wolny.

"Yes. Not far from here," replied Paul.

"We're going there," the officer said. They both drove to the marina. They intentionally stopped near the marina. The boat was not moored there. The officer searched with his flashlight as he approached the shed. The door of the shed was closed. He noticed a crack in the wooden wall of the shed. The officer flashed the light inside the shed. In the stream of illumination, the patrolman noticed a familiar vehicle.

"We need to break the door in," said the officer to Paul; with strong kicks, he broke in the door. "Did Andy have a vehicle?" the officer asked.

"I'm not sure. In all likelihood, probably not. Andy never told me he purchased a car," Paul replied. Officer Wolny walked around the vehicle. Inside the car, he found the registration with currency and a couple of bills, issued to the bakery. While inside the vehicle the patrolmen wrote down the vehicle registration numbers. Later that evening, they drove to the police station.

Lieutenant Wolny entered the police station. He asked to speak to the duty officer. The sergeant on duty entered the scene. They both greeted each other and Wolny explained the situation. He asked if Andy Jaworski had registered his vehicle in his name. The sergeant checked the record. He said that he had not seen Andy registering a vehicle.

"The current registration numbers are from the city of Torun," said the sergeant.

"Will you call the police headquarters of this city and confirm that the bakery exists. Also, check the vehicle registration with the name and with verified numbers?" asked lieutenant Wolny. The sergeant then looked up the phone number for the police headquarters verifying the city and dialed the number. The officer began to talk. It turned out that the vehicle in question was wanted by the police. In connection with the car, the police also were missing a man. There was a specific order warrant to stop them immediately.

The sergeant verified the description given by Paul about the man on Andy's boat. "Thank you. We'll be sure to notify you later," said Wolny to the sergeant. Then they left the building. Outside of the building, Wolny said to Paul, "Andy has escaped with others. It is my duty to announce an alarm. Thank you for notifying us," said the lieutenant to Paul. He drove quickly to the Coast Guard building. Paul then returned home slowly considering the whole situation. It made him anxious. The tension had him lose sleep.

Lieutenant Wolny walked quickly into the building and announced the alarm. On the police radio; he informed the coastguard nearby that was patrolling the sea about the attempt to escape. He gave Andy's boats general description and information of others that may be on board. He also gave the specific names of the escapees. "Stop them immediately! They are dangerous," said the report. Other coastguard stations were also notified of the escape. The race against time was on. Two patrol boats were then dispatched on route to the presumed escape trajectory of Andy's boat.

Captain Murawski was notified about the whole incident. "Peter Mayer is in Ustka. They found the vehicle! The suspect was escaping by boat to Bornholm," said the police officer.

"Deserter! He wanted to run away. I could have arrested him long ago. I'll get him. He will get a bullet in the head," said Murawski. "Inform me about the details regardless of the time," added captain Murawski. He then hung up the phone and went straight to bed.

The wind was increasing in strength, and the waves were getting violently boisterous. The crest of the waves hit the side of the boat. Mary tightly held her frightened children. Peter gave them comfort. Andy maintained the course to Bornholm. It was becoming more difficult. Andy said to Peter, "The waves are pushing us north. It was my intention that we would steadily sail behind one of the cargo ships that left in front of us. The wind delayed our plans. Now in all probability, the coast guard will be looking for us. We have fourteen hours of fuel, but with the inclement weather and boisterous wind, we have only twelve hours. We have lost two hours sailing along the shore. Now the big waves and wind are pushing us north. What can we do?" Andy looked at Peter and waited for an answer.

"You're in command; you know what the absolute best of what we have to do is. Only you know the sea. Let the waves carry us to freedom," said Peter. Andy then turned his head to look at Mary but he could only see her contours in the dark.

He only heard Mary's voice, "We're counting on you to deliver us as our captain to our destiny."

The suspects have been sailing for over five hours. The Baltic Sea, despite its relative size, is considered one of the most dangerous seas in the world. The Sea is shrouded with clouds and darkness. Andy watched with his binoculars. He looked at the horizon where the darkness originated. A bright light was shining in the distance. He noticed predators as he looked at the horizon. "They're chasing us," Andy said to Peter.

The wind changed direction. It was blowing from the west. In addition, more fog began to appear. "It's a good sign for us," said Peter. "The fog will cause us to disappear from their eyes." They sailed on a completely different course than what they had originally intended. Instead of sailing northwest, they sailed north. They did not observe the warning light in front of the boat. It was turned off for their safety. The Polish coast guard and fishing boat would then not see them. They completely depended upon the compass which Andy used. It was dangerous, slow, but safe, According to the observation of Andy's knowledge, they were near the borderline of the territorial waters of Poland. The fog began to grow ever thicker. Mary prayed fervently. Andrew and Margaret began to vomit. The children had become seasick. Mary tried to calm them down and gave them drinking water which did little to settle their stomachs. Andy was at the helm and Peter was standing nearby. Mary sat with her children, huddled in the corner on a small bench hidden within the boat.

A large reflector light lit up the air in front of the Coast Guard boat. They had not seen anyone. The commander of the coast guard boat ordered the soldiers to take their weapons and stand attentively at the bow. "Be alert and ready. Refugees are dangerous. They are wanted by the police. They can have weapons and will shoot without warning," said the commanding officer. One of the soldiers, standing on the prow of the patrol boat prayed quietly that the escapees fleeing would not come across his boat. He silently hoped they would escape. The refugees all dreamed about a better life without the snare of communism.

The commander then noticed a fog in the distance and said, "Come on with it. We will never find them in the cover of this dense fog. Their small boat could only go to Bornholm. I hope we can catch them. The coastguard is looking for them." The crew did not realize that Andy had changed direction to the north. The patrol boats were now moving away from Andy's boat.

The refugees sailed on steadily for an hour in the fog. Andy surmised that they were far beyond the territorial waters of Poland. The wind did not abate. Darkness reigned supremely. You could only hear the rumble of the working engine and the waves bounce on the sides of the boat.

Andy and Peter were desperately searching through the dense fog for safety. The passengers sailed without the aid of a warning light. They did not believe anyone would cross the wake of their course. Collision with the other ship now would be catastrophic. Andy was not alone. He had the responsibility of Mary, the children, and Peter, who was standing nearby. He knew at once that those passengers, although known briefly had the same eventful purpose as him, freedom. The family trusted him ultimately with their lives. Andy ordered everyone to wear a life vest. Peter pulled a vest from the storage compartment and said, "There are only four."

"You put them on. I know how to swim," said Andy. Peter handed Mary one of the vests. He also secured the life preservers on Andrew and little Margaret who were sleeping. Finally, Peter put on the last vest.

The Family sailed during the night. Peter and Andy talked and did not sleep. Mary dozed off, holding Andrew and Margaret. A strange sound echoed near them. They both began to listen and stare at the dense blanket of fog. "It's a ship, but where are they?

I can't see them," said Andy. His heart began to pound loudly. He knew what would threaten their freedom. Andy did not know which way to make the maneuver to avoid a collision. Staring at the thick murky fog in the last second, Andy noticed the light at the stern of a mighty ship.

The huge ship was sailing straight at them! Peter shouted in terror, "Ship, dead ahead!"

Mary was not clear about what was happening; until she saw the bow of a large ship fast approaching within close proximity. She shouted, "God, save us." Andrew and little Margaret were too weak and surprised to call out clutching Roxy. Twenty yards from them, the huge ship began its final approach straight at them. Andy abruptly turned the wheel to the right and pressed hard on the gas. The boat tilted violently to the left. The rising waves listed over the boat, dangerously. The huge ship hit the boat with the fugitives. The boat began to swing violently to the left and to the right. The boat was now rocking dangerously. The powerful force of the ship pushed them and almost capsized them with huge waves. The waves began to break into their boat. Mary and the children were screaming. Peter grabbed the railing. Andy tried to keep his composure. There was nothing he could do. Everyone believed it was over.

The huge ship was moving at its highest speed, as it passed in front of the eyes of the refugees. They all behaved as if they saw a ghost. Their hearts were beating loudly, fear overwhelmed them. As the ship passed the fugitives; the force of the propeller sucked Andy's boat down into a vortex. The boat spun circularly in the waves, violently turning over and finally down within the waves. When the boat tilted, it sank into the dark water. Panic reigned in the small cabin. The power of the water ripped open two doors in the cabin. Terror held them; no one was in control of themselves. Peter saw only the horrified witness of Mary; who was now shouting, "Save the children!" Water began to flow into the cabin and ripped through the doors. Peter desperately tried to grab Mary; but the water pulled her and the children out of the cabin, together with Roxy who was paddling. Everyone was in the water.

The giant ship slowly moved away from the place of the accident. It was a cargo ship. Peter was thrust into the surface of the water. Darkness enveloped and surrounded him. Disoriented; he looked around and shouted, "Mary, where are you?" He searched the turbulent water with terrified eyes in search for his family. "Mary! Mary, where are you?" Peter cried out.

Behind him, he heard, "Peter, I am here!" Mary called out, choking with water. She was 20 yards away, from him.

He swam quickly to her. "Are you all right?" asked Peter.

"Where are the children?" asked Mary, who was choking and desperate.

"Andrew! Margaret!" shouted Peter. Fear and resignation consumed in his eyes. He did not want to think about losing his family.

The voice of a crying child pierced the silence of the water. "It's Margaret," said Mary, in desperation. "Save her!" Peter turned his head towards the sound of the voice. He noticed the shape of an empty life jacket in the distance. Peter swam quickly towards the vest. The small head of Margaret was in the middle of the vest. She was terrified, in shock and crying. Water flooded around her face. Peter lifted her up and pulled her close.

Coughing and spitting up water, Margaret grabbed him by the neck so tightly that Peter could barely breathe. It was a child's helpless body. "Mary! I got her!" shouted Peter.

"Come here!" Mary shouted with happiness. Peter swam to Mary and gave her little Margaret. Mary caught her in her arms and kissing her face and body. Both of them floated; helplessly, on the surface of the water; securely dressed in vests.

"Where is Andrew? Where is Andy?" asked Peter.

"I do not know," said Mary. "Find Andrew." Peter looked around in peril. He searched the surface of the water. "Andrew! Andy!" shouted Peter, several times. He was swimming frantically in different directions beating the water.

Andy was painfully aware of how critical the situation had become. As the boat had overturned, Andy clutched the steering wheel. The water began to break apart the small cabin. He witnessed the violent strength of the water ripping the door from both sides of the frame and Andy thought, "Oh, no. God save us." He was the only one who did not have a life jacket. Being in the water, the whirlwind of the propeller pulled him into the abyss of dark void. Andy was a very good swimmer. He knew how to behave in the water. With the last ounce of his strength, he made a few critical moves and aggressively swam towards the surface of the water. Once he swam above the water; he began to breathe heavily, gasping and choking, overcome by salt water.

There, was a mist and a continued veil of fog. He did not see anyone. Andy began to look around and listen. Andy heard the voice of Peter, "Mary Where Are You?"

"They were alive. What about the children?" Andy wondered. He slowly began to swim toward the voice. Andy was 40 to 50 yards from Peter, swimming in his direction; he located a floating object in the water. "This is the door of my boat. This is our salvation." Andy said to himself. He lay down on them. He began to swim towards Peter. Then Andy noticed a floating vest. He frantically started rowing with his arms. When Andy was near the vest, he noticed Andrew in his life jacket. He lay motionless in shock on the water, with his arms extended. He immediately put Andrew on one of the doors from the boat.

Andy heard Mary and Peter calling each other. He then heard Peter crying out, "Andrew; Andy."

Andy shouted back… "I'm here! I found Andrew."

Peter heard Andy's voice and was very happy. His heart jumped with joy and shouted, "I'm swimming to you." He started swimming towards Andy with all his strength. Andy and Andrew slowly came into his sight. Peter noticed Andrew was lying still on the door of Andy's boat. Andy performed compressions on Andrew's chest. "What's wrong with him?" asked Peter, who was terrified.

"He's done. He's overcome with hyperthermia and shock. It's likely he is unconscious and his lungs filled with water," said Andy.

"We need to work on him," said Peter.

"I'm doing it right now," said Andy.

"Where is Mary?" Andy asked.

"She is not far away," said Peter.

"It would be better for her to be with us. Tell her to swim in our direction. I cannot leave Andrew. I have to save him," said Andy. Then Peter began to call Mary to swim toward them. He then began to swim in her direction like a raving madman; thinking about Andrew and the rest of the family.

Mary swam slowly, along with Margaret. Hearing Peter shouting her name, Mary answered him, "I am here. I am swimming towards you." Shortly, Mary witnessed a terrified face. It was Peter. She asked, "What happened?"

"It's a bad scene with Andrew. He is not breathing! He must have been underwater for an extended time. Andy is trying to do CPR to revive him." Peter responded.

Mary was very excited and was beginning to panic. She said, "Take me quickly to him. I must be with him. I cannot lose him." Peter helped her swim as quickly as possible so that both of them would be with Andrew. Swimming back, he kept called out to Andy so that he would not get lost.

Peter held Margaret and swam with Mary to Andy. She noticed Andrew lying on the door of Andy's boat. He continued in faith to bring Andrew back to life. Seeing his life return, Mary began to touch gently the face of her child. She began to say in a crying voice, "My beloved son, do not leave us. We are with you. God give him his spirit. I cannot lose him. Please, have mercy on his life. Return his life to him." At that moment Andrew started coughing and vomiting out sea water. Andy quickly turned him on his side. Andrew coughed and expelled more water from his mouth. Completely exhausted, he began to weep and cry out. "Hush my dear one, be still. I'm with you," said Mary. Peter witnessing this devotion began to rejoice with happiness.

He started to embrace Andy and thanked him warmly. Peter said, "I'll never forget what you did to save the life of my son Andrew. I knew that I could count on you."

The sun came up on the horizon. Stillness covered the surface of the water. Peter, Mary, Andrew, little Margaret and Andy become castaways. Gathered together, as one group they stayed alive, in the water, thanks to their life jackets. Only Andy did not have his. He was an excellent swimmer. Water in the Baltic Sea at this time of the year was warm. A healthy human body could bear this. It was now the end of summer. Peter laid little Margaret next to Andrew on the floating door. Holding each other desperately, clutching around the door, they breathed deeply. They had just survived the worst event. There was a moment of silence. Andy said, "The morning fog remained, but soon the sun will be higher in the sky and the fog will disappear. We need to look around."

"Where is the boat?" Peter asked.

"I do not know. I did not see it," replied Andy.

"We have to remain vigilant. There are many ships which can create havoc and ram us. Peter, give me your vest. I'll look around and maybe I will find something that can float that was left of the boat," said Andy.

"Andy, you saved Andrew and us from a terrible tragedy. What happened was not your fault, we thank you wholeheartedly, and you'll always be our friend. You must not blame yourself," said Mary and took hold of Andy's hand, in thanks. Peter took off his life vest and handed it to Andy.

"We will call out to you so that we will not lose contact with each other," said Peter.

"Okay," said Andy. Andy put on the vest. He experienced great relief. At last, something sustained him. Andy rested for a moment.

Andrew, to everyone's surprise, said, "Can you find Roxy? He is the family dog. We can't lose him. He's here somewhere. Save him. Please." No one noticed seeing the dog.

"I will look for him," Andy said. After a while, Andy floated away and disappeared into the mist.

Every minute Peter cried out loud, "Andy!"

Andy answered, "I'm here." Andy did not know in what direction to swim. He was looking for the remains of his boat. The impact may have injured him. After a moment, he saw a water bottle. He swam to it. It was the buyout supply that Peter brought along. "There were definitely more of them," thought Andy. He remembered that there were twelve water bottles in the box that was on the boat. He grabbed the bottled water and put it in his life vest. Andy then resumed his search.

Mary and Peter were waiting impatiently for Andy's return. "I should go to help him," said Peter.

"Do not leave me alone with the children. I'm tired of treading water," said Mary, who was afraid.

Andrew said in a low tone of voice, "Drink. I'm thirsty."

"Son, sorry we do not have a supply of water. You have to wait for additional water," Mary said, in pain, as doubt and circumstances overwhelmed her. Mary could not give the children what they wanted. Little Margaret squeezed Mary's hand tightly; she was dehydrated, thirsty and hungry. Peter and Mary were making an extra effort to encourage their children. Mary, looking at Peter with her tired horrified eyes, asked, "What will happen to us now?"

"Only God knows. We're waiting for Andy. He is the most capable man and well oriented to handle this terrible situation; in which we find ourselves. Remember all of what you claimed before the escape. You had a good feeling, it's overwhelming. We must believe that everything will ultimately end well. Do you believe this?" asked Peter as he stared into Mary's eyes.

"I have to remain and believe. I have no other choice," said Mary looking at the weakened and frightened children. "What are the children guilty of, that they must endure so much pain and misery only to live with our final decision?"

"Remember wars do not last, tough people do. Turmoil is all in your mind. Think of this as a bad dream. You are tough, strong, and the most incredible woman I have ever known. We will get through this," Peter pleaded with Mary.

Peter communicated with Andy. After 10 minutes Peter heard from Andy, "I'm coming back." A great relief calmed the conviction of Mary and Peter. Adamantly, they stared in the direction that Andy should emerge. Peter noticed Andy, swimming with great effort. He was pulling an object; it was debris from the wreckage. Peter swam to help him. Andy had two boards and a few objects pressed into a vest. "I found something to eat and fresh water," Andy said.

"That's good," said Peter. "The children needed water, especially Andrew. Let me help you." Peter retrieved the boards from Andy; secured himself to the boards and slowly swam towards Mary.

Andrew looked at Andy and asked, "Did you find Roxy?"

"I'm very sorry, but I did not find my dog, Roxy," Andy replied. Andrew's face remained sad. Andy pulled out from behind the vest a bottle of water, three apples and a small jar of jam that Mary carried on the road. The first thing Mary did was open the bottle and give water to Andrew. He drank it quickly with fatigue. When he finished, he laid his head against the door. Margaret also drank. Then each of them enjoyed the jam with a few sips of water. The children were happy. They had to save food and water. They did not know how long they would be in this situation.

Finally, the children were quiet. "Do anyone of you want jam?" asked Mary.

"No. Save it for the children. They need strength," said Andy.

"What are we going to do now?" asked Mary?

Andy said, "We must wait until it is completely clear and the fog disappears. Then we will see what remains of our boat".

"Do you know where you are?" Mary asked Andy.

"I do not have a clue. Definitely not in the beleaguered territory of Poland," said Andy and continued, "We have to select important items that would be good for food and drink. You brought a full bag of food into the boat," said Andy looking at Mary.

"It is not about us. It's about the children. We will survive. There were 12 bottles of water in the cabin. If you found only one, there are probably others if they did not shatter." Mary responded.

The survivors talked about the incident, with the ship. "How did it happen; that no one on the ship saw us?" wondered Mary.

Andy said, "At night, everyone is in the ship and there is no one on deck. Apparently, they did not see or hear a word. There was a mist and darkness. Our boat was very small and their ship was huge. The difference in height created the opportunity for survival."

The family was waiting for a sign from heaven, the sun. At last the sun began to brighten. The sun began to break through the fog. Everyone was looking straight ahead; saying they wanted to see a sign that would delight their hearts. The fog slowly melted away. Yard by yard, they saw more and more open space around them. The water was now calm as a mirror. 20 yards, 30 yards ... 50 yards. Mary shouted, "I see something." Andy and Peter turned their heads to the space in front of Mary. They had a wide expression in their eyes. A large object raised out of the water.

"That is my boat," shouted Andy, as he began swimming towards the boat.

On the way, Andy noticed a few pieces of wood from his boat's side, with three bottles of water, which he placed in behind his vest. After a long swim, Andy arrived at his boat. The boat was capsized, halfway above the water. The bow rose slightly up; the back of the boat was in the water. Andy knew but he had not made a statement before that his boat was a standard wooden work. If the boat has not been completely destroyed, it could remain on the surface of the water. The engine is only one portion of the boat. It can be submerged in the water but the rest will stay on the surface of the water. He was not at all wrong.

Being near the capsized boat Andy spotted a dog's head. "Roxy," called Andy. The dog rose above the water to his feet and began wagging his tail and making a friendly whimper. Andy was pleased to see Roxy. Immediately, he thought of Andrew and Margaret. "They will certainly be happy to see the dog," he thought for himself. After a few minutes, the remainder of the survivors slowly approached the capsized boat. "Roxy is here!" called Andy.

Andrew's eyes widened and he began to shout, "Roxy, Roxy. Where are you?" Mary and Peter rejoiced at the news from Andy. The children will have their friend in these difficult times. "I want Roxy," Andrew said. Margaret's face overjoyed smiled at the sight of the dog.

"You must wait until Uncle Andy has made sure that it is safe to get the dog," said Mary. At the word, "Uncle," Andy looked at Mary, smiled, and said, "We are family?" Everyone was cheered up by his words. "We are family," said Mary with a smile.

Andy inspected the boat from all sides. "I knew he did not sink. I could count on him," said Andy; almost crying he added, "We're saved. We now have a better opportunity for survival." Mary rejoiced with happiness.

After a brief rest, Andy took off his life jacket and dove into the dark water. After a minute, he floated to the surface of the water with a roll of rope. Andy rested for a short period and looked toward Peter. "I need your help. There are three canisters blocked under the water. We need to release them," said Andy. Peter looked at Mary.

Mary said, "Go." They both dived. After a while, three canisters flooded to the surface and come up behind them. They rested a while, after the dive.

"I have a small compartment in which I have stored four cans of fish. This was always my backup supply." Andy said and dove again and after some time he floated with four cans in his hand and a small knife. "This will be useful for us to open the canned food. So now we have three bottles of water, three apples, and four cans of fish and one jar of jam. Enough for the children. We'll survive. Water is the most important item for us. Let me rest," said Andy, who was tired.

Andy and Peter were questioning what to do next. "We now have two options," said Andy. "The first is to climb on top of the boat and wait for help. The second is, in case of an emergency, we must build a small raft made of three canisters, these two boards; and the door on which the children lie. We must prepare and have hope."

"Why a raft?" asked Mary.

"We will try to get on top of the boat. If the boat beginnings to sink, we'll have a raft," Andy stated.

"I understand," said Mary.

"We'll build the raft first. Give me a rope," said Andy to Peter. When Peter handed him the rope, Andy cut the rope into five pieces. He tied two ends of the boards to the first canister. Peter helped Andy in their activities. Andy tied the second and third canister to the end of each board. "Now we're going to put canisters under the door where Andrew and Margaret are lying. A small raft was created in the shape of a triangle with the other items. It will be safer and more stable for children, and for us. We will be able to keep to our plan if necessary. It will be then easier for us to stay on the surface of the water."

Mary tightly held Margaret and Andrew's hands in the event that they would panic. Andy grabbed the end of one board and Peter did the same to the other board and they took positions on both sides of the door on which the children were laid. "Mother I am afraid," said Andrew seeing what was going on. He held Mary's hand with all his might.

"Do not be scared. We're all with you," said Mary encouraging the frightened children.

"We will place the boards at the ends of the floating door. Understand?" Andy asked Peter.

"Yes, I understand," said Peter.

Andy began to count, "One, two, and three." They both dipped the ends of the boards into the water and pushed them under the ends of the door. The canisters gave resistance. The primitive raft swayed and rose freely over the water. Andrew and little Margaret were above the water and did not have to risk their lives in the water.

"Andy, you invented this wonderfully," said Mary. "You are a genius."

Andy and Peter rested. "I will try to get to the top of the boat. We will see what will happen." Andy said as he began to carefully pull himself on top of the boat. The boat moved slightly and tilted, and yet remained stable. Andy was moving higher and higher on the bottom of the boat. For the first time in almost three hours, his body was not in the water. Warmth and great relief flooded through his tired body. He reached the highest crest on the top ridge of the boat. Roxy seeing his master began to bark with happiness and lick his hand. "Everything will be fine, Roxy," said Andy. "So far the boat held steady," Andy thought to himself.

"Mary, it is your turn to come in here; then the children and finally you Peter. We will all stay alive if we maintain self-control," said Andy.

Andrew and Margaret began to cry when Mary went away from them. "Mother, don't leave us!" shouted Andrew.

"Do not be afraid, I'm with you. You'll be with your mother, soon. I promise you," said Peter.

Andy slowly slid down to the lowest point of the capsized boat. Mary swam to the boat and stretched out her hand. Andy with a firm strong quick effort pulled her out of the water. "Get up and hold the ridge of the boat," said Andy to Mary.

"Peter, give me Margaret and Andrew." Margaret began to cry out with fear when Peter handed her to Andy. He picked her up and slowly delivered her to Mary. Margaret embraced Mary and stopped crying.

"Don't cry. You are with me," said Mary. The same happened with Andrew. Being in Mary's embrace, Andrew was content and safe, he squeezed Roxy. The operation of transferring children from the raft went quickly and was successful. Peter tied one end of the last piece of rope to the primitive raft. The other end was thrown to Andy. Peter was the last one to climb to the top of the hull.

The boat sank deeper into the water under the weight of the survivors and began to tilt, listing gently to both sides and after few moments; stabilized. For the first time, they sat on something dry. They felt safe. Mary began to laugh. Andy and Peter looked at her, in surprise. Mary looked at them and said with a laugh, "We are sitting on our deserted island and waiting for help." Everyone began to laugh at this unusual humor. Peter pulled out a bottle of water, opened it and drank a sip. Then Peter gave water to Andy and he drank. The water was refreshing and sweet. Andy gave the water to Mary. She first gave water to the children. Then she poured some water in her hand, giving it to Roxy. Only a few sips of water remained for Mary.

Everyone floated in silence, holding the ridge of the boat. Andy and Peter looked around. "What now?" asked Peter as he looked at Andy?

Andy thought about it for a while and said, "We do not have any other choice, but be patient and wait. Two things can happen, one good and the other bad."

"Let's believe for a good outcome," said Mary.

"The Polish ship may see us first; the Captain will take us aboard and transport us directly to Poland. You all know, very well, what awaits us there. We don't want to go back to Poland," Andy said with a firm voice.

Mary began to pray loudly, "God send us help; someone who will open a path, the door to freedom." All were in agreement with Mary.

The sun penetrated higher and higher. Andy looked within the horizon in search of any help. Mary and Peter were taking care of the children. "I'm hungry," said Andrew. Peter opened one can of herring in oil and fed his hungry children. Mary gave them some water and both children soon fell asleep. Margaret fell asleep on Mary's knees and Andrew in the arms of Peter. Hours passed and nothing eventful happened. The survivors in boredom did not know where they were. They were waiting for help and the favor of God.

The Polish coastguard patrol boats pursued the escapees vigilantly. Maintaining, coordinating and connecting with other divisions. The escapees were not found. "They are on the open sea lost, hidden in the mist," said one of the officers on the boat.

They had time and diligence to continue the search. The patrol boats did not realize that the tide cared Andy's boat far away from them. They were not sailing on to Bornholm.

In the coast guard office, they received reports from four additional patrol boats that they had not found the refugees. Lieutenant Wolny was just finishing his desk duty; giving all messages to his subordinate and said, "Looks like they escaped. Four boats chased them. Fog helped them to escape. Possibly the tide altered their course to the north. They did not have enough fuel. They had a small engine and small capacity. There are many unexplained questions. We will get a reprimand from the administration. I feel it in my bones," said Wolny to his friend.

The phone rang. The lieutenant picked up the phone and said, "Lieutenant Wolny."

"I am Captain Murawski from the police headquarters of Torun." Wolny listened, intently on the phone. "Do you have the escapees?"

"Not yet," Wolny replied.

"Why not? How well do you guard the borders," Murawski shouted and added, "Get it done. I'm calling Warsaw," and hung up.

Wolny said to himself, "The next idiot is indeed wise." After a few minutes, Wolny said goodbye to the alternate and left the building.

The Swedish fishing boat industry then sailed inland towards the natural waters of the Baltic Sea to catch herring. One boat of six fishermen was sitting on the deck preparing their nets.

The captain was at the helm with binoculars and saw something in the distance. He shouted to one of the fishermen, "Officer Olaf, come here to the bridge." Olaf came and stood at the forward position of the helm. The captain took the binoculars and stared again at the horizon. "Castaways in the water!" said the Captain. The alert crew stood up and stared at the horizon. "Full speed ahead," said the Captain. The boat moved with top speed. All were alert and were in the survey.

It was now 10 am in the morning. Andy surveyed the horizon. Peter and Mary were holding the children. Andy shouted, "Boat!" Mary and Peter were looking at the solitary point indicated by Andy. Indeed, something was fast approaching, towards the south. Everyone began to wave their arms. Mary silently prayed and said over and over, "Let it be the Swedes. Let it be the Swedes, not Poles." Everyone stared at the horizon watching the boat intently.

Now began a nervous, uncertain time. They thought, "Who could it be?" The refugees waited impatiently. Andy had a good eye. After half an hour Andy said, "Could this be a fishing boat from Sweden?" Great relief prevailed for the first time in Mary's heart. She survived the escape primarily because of her hope for her children. She had already lost two children during the war; Mary would not lose her devoted family again. They were precious to her. She watched them with a watchful desperate eye at all times.

The Swedish fishing boat slowly approached the refugees; sitting on the top of their capsized boat. The captain began to speak to them in a language which they did not understand. Peter understood the problem; he now attempted to speak in German, "Does anyone speak German?"

"I speak German fluently," said one of the fishermen. They both started speaking German. The fisherman's name was Knud. Peter explained to him that they were in a turbulent situation and had escaped from Poland to seek asylum.

Knud explained everything to the captain; whose name was Gottfried. "I will have no other choice but to notify the Coastguard," said Gottfried which is what he immediately did. The Swedes moored to the capsized boat with great caution. Five minutes later and with Andy's and Peter's help, everyone was on the Swedish fishing boat. The Captain asked them, "What happened to the boat?" Peter told them all the stories and events leading up to the accident. "You were so lucky that the big ship did not ram you," said Gottfried. There was no end to the discussion of every information that could go wrong on the open seas.

The Swedish Coastguard boat arrived. One of the officers came on aboard the fishing boat and with Knud's help translated everything. He asked Peter many questions. The refugees became castaways and asked for political asylum. The coastguard officer ordered all the refugees to board the Coastguard boat. Peter thanked the fishermen for their earnest help and asked Knud for his address. Knud eagerly gave him his address.

When the Coastguard officer checked the identity of the survivors, the polish cargo ship passed within close range. One of the Coastguard officers asked, "Do you want to get on this ship, and go back to Poland?"

Peter replied firmly, "No! We did not run away and risk our lives to simply give up or resign ourselves to go back to Poland. They're waiting for us; they will give us either prison or death."

"I understand," said the officer as he finished his duty. Peter, Mary, and Andy knew that they were very blessed. If the Polish ship encountered them earlier than the Swedes, the family would now be on their way to Poland.

Leaving Andy's capsized boat in the open sea, threatened the shipping lines at sea. The Coast Guard made an effort to tow Andy's boat to the nearest port. The boat could not withstand the pressure of the water and movement. The tide finally caused it to sink. Andy, together with Peter and Mary watched the boat disappear into the dark abyss of the sea. The little boat served them well and gave them the freedom that the family desperately deserved.

It was a beautiful sunny day on September 1, 1949. Peter held Andrew in his arms; Mary tightly held little Margaret and Andy with Roxy sailed into their dream of freedom.

Chapter XX
Freedom

TWO MONTHS PASSED. PETER and his family with their friend Andy and his dog Roxy left Sweden and sailed on an oceangoing passenger ship to America. Klaus paid for all the tickets. After a long journey, the passengers of the ship saw the eventful land of promise America, Ellis Island. They underwent full medical examinations. Immigrants have been subjected to rigorous examinations to avoid any disease entering the U.S. Then Peter and his family entered the ferry with other passengers and were transported to the mainland United States of America.

The ferry left Ellis Island and moored in the harbor of New York. The passengers exited to the Promised Land. Peter was lifting Andrew with one hand and in the other a suitcase. Mary was carrying Margaret. Andy was holding in one hand two large oversized suitcases and in the other he held Roxy. They were walking into their dreamland. Peter and Mary were very excited to meet with their old friends which they had not seen for over six years. After a long moment, Peter heard someone's voice calling him from afar, "Peter! Mary!" Peter turned his head in the direction of the voice. First, he noticed Klaus, waving his hands. The couple moved towards Klaus. Peter, his wife Mary and their children embraced Klaus, Gertrude, and Horst. Horst, who is now an old man, was walking with a cane.

Peter introduced Andy, his faithful and trustworthy friend, who helped them escape from Poland. To everyone's delight, Andrew presented his loyal dog, Roxy. There was now no end to their joy. The assembled families rejoiced with relief. Klaus carried the suitcases. Peter squeezed Andrew's hand, and Mary handed little Margaret to Gertrude and they all went to the cars waiting for them in the parking lot. Mary, who was anxious, literally opened freely her hands. She hadn't done that for weeks. They hurt from carrying little Margaret. Everyone walked slowly and realized that Horst couldn't keep up with them.

Three of his friends came with their vehicles to take them and their luggage to Klaus' home. After one hour, they stopped in front of a large house. There was an open grove of trees, fields and grass. "This is our home and your home," Horst said, who continued, "I am old. I live on the first floor. Klaus and his family live on the second; you all will live on the third floor." They all went inside the home. Peter and Mary met Klaus' two children, the elder Paul, and the younger Stanley. The heavy luggage was carried to the third floor where Peter was to live, with his family.

They had three bedrooms, two bathrooms, a kitchen, and a spacious living room. There was new furniture in the apartment. Mary could not help to admire the splendor she saw in front of her. It was now a different world. "Let's go downstairs to Horst and have dinner," Klaus said. Andy secured a room on the first floor right next to Horst. At dinner, Peter thanked Andy for his trust. Without his help and assistance, they would not be in the United States.

Peter said to him, "I have kept my promise to you. You are in America with us; you are part of our family." Andy began to cry convulsive tears with emotion. He knew about America, but he could not think or imagine he would ever come here.

After dinner, Peter began to tell the account of his story... when they talked about the death of John, Vladek and Hans they started to cry all over again. They were overcome with deep emotion. Three hours passed and Horst said, "You are tired. Now go to sleep; tomorrow we will talk again." Everyone stood up and said their goodbyes and went to their rooms.

Andrew and Margaret slept in their own room with Roxy. An hour passed before Peter and Mary lay in a big oversized bed. "At last we are free. Our dreams were fulfilled," said Peter and fell asleep. Mary hugged Peter and fell asleep too.

The following day, Gertrude and Mary took the children and went to a nearby park. Peter, Andy, Klaus, and Horst sat alone in the living room and considered making the right decision for Peter's family with Andy. Here, Peter told them how he received a fortune from Andrew. He carried the fortune sewn into his clothes. Then Horst said, "You do not have to worry about money, we have a fortune. All the money, principle and savings from the Swiss bank I have transferred directly to our bank."

Peter said, "Hans has given me all his savings, which he had, and placed it in a Swiss bank."

"That's very good. Hans was a good man and a trusted friend," said Horst.

Klaus joined the conversation and said, "First, Peter must receive all the necessary papers. Documents must be signed before patrons can go to the bank."

A month passed and Peter's family with Andy became accustomed to life in a new country. They learned English, which they intended to use for the rest of their lives. Finally, Klaus and Horst took Peter to the bank. At the bank, Peter presented the relevant documents that were necessary with identification so that all of Hans' savings in the Swiss bank would then be transferred into his name. After two weeks, Peter received a letter of intent from the bank. At dinner, Peter opened the letter and saw "the amount you received from Hans is 150,000, francs." It was a small fortune!

Peter, Mary, Andy, Klaus, Gertrude, Horst and their children formed one, big happy family. Together they opened their company which brought them great financial benefits. All lived happily ever after.

Chapter XXI
Conclusion

CAPTAIN MURAWSKI COULD NOT forgive himself for failing to arrest Peter and his family. Kozlowski was happy that he was the main and proud owner of the entire bakery. He got a promised contract with a military unit to deliver bread and shared the entire profit with Murawski.

Approximately a year after Peter escaped, an unknown and strange mysterious man came anonymously with a small package to Charles. When Charles opened it, he began to cry with Sophie. There were two photos of Peter with his extended family. The letter described the course as well as details of the escape, which Peter dedicated his life to overcome. There was also an envelope for Charles. He opened it and was speechless. A $1,000 bankroll! This was a fortune in those times in Poland.

Charles was fired from the bakery. He never told Kozlowski the truth of what he learned. He did not confess the trust and confidence that he had with Peter, to Murawski. In the spring of 1952, he opened his grocery store.

In 1989, communism was destined to fall in Poland. Peter, Klaus and Andy's families visited Poland in 1990. They met with their extended family and friends who helped them throughout their very difficult time of escape. The house which Peter and Mary built with their own hands before the war was standing in the same place, but was owned by the immediate family of Captain Murawski. Peter Mayer never saw Kozlowski again. Kozlowski died long before Peter visited Poland. The bakery with its memories had been demolished. Now standing there are only local buildings. Charles was retired and together with Sophie gave shelter and care to their grandchildren with their memories.

--THE END

Dear Reader,

"If you enjoyed my book, I would truly appreciate if you left a review so others can receive the same benefits you have. Your review will allow me to better serve you and all my other readers even more."

Sincerely, Jacob